THE
FUTURE OF
HUMAN
HEREDITY

◇◇

*An Introduction to Eugenics
in Modern Society*

FREDERICK OSBORN

WEYBRIGHT AND TALLEY

New York

To my wife

Published in the United States by
WEYBRIGHT AND TALLEY, INC.
3 East 54th Street,
New York, New York 10022.

Library of Congress Catalog Card No. 68-12870

PRINTED IN THE UNITED STATES OF AMERICA

STR595│300│4│18│68

Foreword

For centuries and even millennia, man worked to improve the breeds of his domesticated animals and plants. In stark contrast, the genetic endowment of mankind itself has been neglected almost entirely. Eugenics is an applied science aiming to end this neglect. Eugenics was defined by Galton, in 1883, as "The study of the agencies under social control that may improve or impair the racial qualities of future generations either physically or mentally." Today we would use the word "genetic" in place of Galton's "racial".

Ironically enough, the advancement of eugenics was

hindered more often by its overzealous proponents than by its opponents. Human physical and mental characteristics, like those of any other organism, are products of developmental processes in which both genetic and environmental variables play important roles. Some eugenists chose to believe heredity to be all-powerful and environment negligible. Even worse, eugenics has been and, in places, is still being used as an apology for race and class biases. Eugenics in America has unfortunately not escaped this misuse. As Mr. Osborn states, "In both the national legislation resulting in the quota act, and the state legislation on sterilization, the eugenic argument had been overworked. The evidence for heredity was based on inadequate studies, and racial prejudices corrupted the nature of the evidence . . . When later Hitler prostituted eugenics, the American public was ready to drop the word from its vocabulary." Other kinds of eugenical visionaries came forward with apocalyptic prophecies of an imminent genetic breakdown of the human species, and with Brave New World projects to escape so dire a fate.

And yet eugenics has a sound core. The real problem which mankind will not be able to evade indefinitely is where the evolutionary process is taking man, and where man himself wishes to go. Mr. Osborn has for several decades been the clear-sighted leader of the eugenical movement in America, who strove to make the substance of eugenics scientific and its name respectable again. Gently but firmly he opposed the overzealous partisans who worked themselves up to states of frenzy. And with no less restraint and firmness, he insisted that eugenics is not to be regarded as a luxury but as a necessity. His wisdom and moderation have helped to overcome the damage caused by the excessive enthusiasm of some eugenists. Here is a eugenist who not merely admits but stresses the importance of human environments for human development! According to Osborn, "The measures envisaged by the eugenist for raising the genetic level are also measures envisaged by the environmentalist for raising the level of the environment in which children are reared. It makes no difference which is the more important, both are taken into account. Each improvement in genetic capacity enables the individual to take better advantage of the improved environment, and the average of developed and measurable intelligence and character is raised accordingly in each generation."

The Future of Human Heredity gives a simple and concise statement of its author's considered judgments of what eugenics was, is, and ought to be. It deserves to be widely read and carefully pondered.

THEODOSIUS DOBZHANSKY
The Rockefeller University, 1967

Contents

Foreword   v

Introduction   1

1   *Selection and Survival*   6
    Survival of Family Lines among Primitive Hunters
    and Food Gatherers 1,000,000 B.C. to
    8,000 B.C.   6
    Survival among Agricultural Peoples Since
    8,000 B.C.   13

2   *The United States, 1865–1965 Survival of Family*
    Lines in an Industrialized Modern State   19
    The Spread of Birth Control and its Effect on
    Survival   19

Contents

Group Differentials in Births; Their Expansion and
Decline Over the Past Hundred Years 24

Birth Differentials between Different Types of
Individuals 32

3 ⟩ The Genetic Significance of Group and
Individual Birth Differentials 41

Measuring the Heredity Component in Intelligence
and Personality 41

The Index of Opportunity for Selection 53

Genetic Change Resulting from Group
Differentials in Births 56

Genetic Change as a Result of Differences in Size
of Family between Individuals 58

4 ⟩ Defects and Abnormalities 63

Evidence for Relaxed Selection 64

The Physical Basis of Heredity 70

The Frequency of Defects and Abnormalities 73

Genetic Equilibrium and the Genetic Load 79

5 ⟩ Eugenic Policies and Proposals 83

The Chronology of Eugenic Proposals 83

Proposals for the Reduction of Defects 89

Proposals for Raising the Level of Intelligence 98

6 ⟩ The Future of Human Heredity 107

References 119
Index 131

Introduction

Eugenics is concerned with the changes which may be taking place in human heredity. In more scientific language, it is concerned with the frequency and distribution of different types of genetic factors in successive generations of human populations. Essentially eugenics seeks to understand and ultimately to direct the forces that control human inheritance through matings, births, and deaths.

The idea of eugenics derived from Darwin's theory of evolution, first established in *The Origin of Species*. If man is the product of a long evolutionary process, there is every reason to believe that man in his present form is only at a certain stage in his development, and still subject to change. The direction that change will take depends on which of many different types of man survive in our modern, highly controlled environments.

To understand the limitations and the possibilities of the part man may play, consciously or unconsciously, in his own evolution, we must have some knowledge of how human life evolved. Not in the sense of the schoolboy who knows simply that man rose from lower forms, but as part of our thinking about human behavior. We must understand that all sensitivities which inform us of the world about us, all movements of which our muscles are capable, all emotions which may direct our actions, all mental operations which our minds may be taught to handle, are the responses of a physical structure to the stimuli of the environment; that this physical structure is infinitely complex and some parts of it beyond human understanding; that it is different for each individual, and that for each of us it changes with time and experience. We must understand that apart from defects and deficiencies every normal hereditary variation found in man today has been advantageous to survival in one or another of the environments man has lived in during past millennia. In a very real sense man in his infinite variety is the evolutionary product of all his environmental experiences. Heredity and environment are interrelated in the processes of evolution just as they are in the development of the individual.

Evolution was possible because all living things are endowed with a system of inheritance—a genetic system—that makes possible changes in the physical structure from one generation to another. The genetic system was not understood in Darwin's time, and as a result of this ignorance, many erroneous theories have been put forward in the name of eugenics. There was no science of genetics until the rediscovery of Mendel in 1900, and some of the most startling advances in genetics have only been made since 1950. We now know that the development of the physical structure of individuals is directed by a genetic code passed on with modifications by parents to their children. There is a considerable analogy between the genetic code and the taped codes fed into computers. The genetic code carries billions of unit components, combinations of which give "instructions" for their development. No two genetic codes are alike except those of identical twins, and hence no two people except identical twins are alike in their heredity. Development takes place in an environment that is unique for each individual, no two environments being the same. Even identical twins are never entirely alike, but differ to a greater or a less degree in many of their characteristics.

When conception has taken place, each parent has passed on to the newly-fertilized cell only one-half of its genes. These have been chosen at random, one out of every pair of each parent, and the corresponding genes have again paired up in the newly created cell. The progeny has then received half of its genetic code from each parent, not as a mixture, but in discrete units selected at random, each having its special effect on one or more aspects of development and function. Because of the variety of different types of genes scattered throughout the population, the system of bisexual mating makes for an almost infinite number of possible genetic codes, and thus provides the material for change. The potential for change is further increased by mutations, or changes in the composition of the units of heredity, the genes. These changes are occasionally brought about by some mutagenic agent, which may be radiation, a chemical, an infection, or some other force. The mutated or changed genes may then be reproduced in the next generation, and so become part of our genetic inheritance.

Changes that may take place in the kind, distribution, and frequency of genes from one generation to another depend on the differential survival, through differential deaths and births, of different kinds of people carrying different kinds of genes. Gene distribution is also affected by mate selection, to the extent that partners in mating have similar characteristics. Scientific studies of the distribution and rates of births and deaths and mate selection are in the province of the demographer or population specialist.

The study of changes in heredity that may now be taking place requires the collaboration of the geneticist and the demographer. And since there are no direct measures for the genetic component of some of the most important human qualities, such as intelligence and personality, it is also necessary to have the help of the psychologist to measure the external aspects of these qualities and to find out to what extent differences in measurable qualities may be accounted for by variations in heredity.

Thus the applied science of eugenics falls in the province of several scientific disciplines, especially those of genetics, demography, and psychology. Because it is not the responsibility of any one scientific group, eugenics has had less consistent attention than many other less important fields of inquiry. The purpose of this book is to present a brief overview of current eugenic thinking in these various fields, and to suggest the conclusions which can be drawn for human welfare and happiness.

1

Selection and Survival

◇◇◇

Survival of Family Lines among Primitive Hunters and Food Gatherers 1,000,000 B.C. to 8,000 B.C.

Man's ancestry goes back over a billion years to the earliest forms of life on earth. Scientists believe that the first life was a spontaneous development, brought about when the appropriate chemicals found themselves together under just the right temperature, pressure, and physical and chemical environment for such an action of creation. It was only a single

molecule, but it had the power to absorb food and to reproduce itself—it was alive. It could grow, split in two, and leave
descendants. Its reproductive mechanism was the prototype
of all the reproductive mechanisms of all living things today.
It produced only duplicates of itself until, in the slow processes of time, some environmental force, perhaps some errant
radiation, made a slight change in its chemical composition,
and its offspring were no longer exact duplicates of the parental stock. New forms arose. Some survived in one environment, some in another. Some died out. Living things became
more complicated and more diverse. When bisexual forms
arose, changes came more rapidly, new environments became
habitable, and finally life flowered in all its marvelous diversity
of grass and flower and tree, of reptile, fish, and bird, of mammals tinier than a mouse and large as elephants and whales,
of hoofed animals and carnivores and apes, and finally *man*,
so different and yet in many ways so like his many kin.

Our knowledge of evolution comes from fossil remains
and from the similarities and comparisons of the development
of living things, and from an understanding of the genetic
mechanism through which evolution operated. The story of
evolution is far from complete. Scientists agree on the main
outlines, but many details are lacking, and there is still much
discussion about the kind and sequence of events at different
periods. Since eugenics is concerned with man, we may pass
over life's early origins and begin at the point at which man
first began to differ from his early apelike ancestors.

The hominoids first appeared at least two and a half

million years ago, showing a distinctive ability in making and using tools. The first of the new breed were intelligent, social, and exploratory. They were not yet quite men, but fast becoming more than apes. For thousands and thousands of years they kept changing and evolving as they developed new social systems appropriate to their ability to walk upright and use their hands, and to their increasing intelligence. Survival in their new way of life required longer periods of child care. Through the processes of selection and differential survival their brains enlarged as they improved their tools, hunted in new ways and in larger groups, discovered fire, improved their speech. Changes in social organization evolved concurrently with changes in physical heredity. In their dangerous environment even slight improvements in brain or tools or speech or social organization made the difference between survival and the dying out of family lines.[1]

As men increased in numbers and gained greater control of their environments, they spread out into new lands wherever food was available. Fossil remains found in great parts of Africa, Asia, and Europe show men of 250,000 years ago moving in groups over wide areas and using stone hand-axes and flaked tools of standardized makes. Homo sapiens—modern man about as he looks today—seems to have appeared about 45,000 years ago. He spread into the new world some 12,000 or more years later, long before the introduction of agriculture or the domestication of animals.

Among hunters and food gatherers in the wild there is a necessary division of labor between men and women.

Food is shared, both within the family and within the tribal group. Early men cooperated in hunting game, in keeping trespassers off their territory, and in helping each other in the care of their young. Survival favored individuals who had the ability to exercise leadership. Cooperation and generosity became increasingly important to the survival of the group, and the genetic basis for these qualities was extended. But fighting qualities were also necessary for survival, and the conflict between the forces of aggression and those of co-operation is still evident in man today.

The sex urge of early man was not apparently reduced, probably because it continued to have undiminished survival value in the new social environment. Subhuman primates, like humans, mate frequently and to a great extent it was sex that brought the primates together in social groups. But even with primates, sex could lead to deadly fights. In the more complex social structure and the new environments of early man, sex could not be allowed to interfere with the intense struggle to wrest a living from nature, or the need to care for the young. Sex had to be regulated by morals, by rules and regulations and taboos, so that it would not interfere with the cooperative effort necessary to the survival of the group. In the case of sex, control was brought about not so much by change in the genetic nature of man as by social controls. In the words of the anthropologist Marshall Sahlins, "It is notable that repression of sex in favor of other ends is a battle which, while won for the species, is still joined in every individual to this day." [2]

9

During the million years in which man and his proto-types have lived on earth, his survival and that of his children have depended on his intelligence and character, on his physical strength and vitality, and on his endurance. Until he developed agriculture his family and tribal units were necessarily small, and these small populations, or "isolates," made possible rapid evolutionary changes. His death rate was high. Moving cautiously through great forests and plains, in small groups, competing with savage animals for food, sleeping with his mate and children in caves or in the open, inadequately clothed, subject to torrid heat and the bitter cold of winter, plagued by disease and hunger, with no tools except those made by his own hands, few but the strongest survived to middle age.

In the long process of selection, man attained the physical and mental potentials that characterize the majority of men today. He developed the kind of brain that can handle the complicated technical processes of our modern society, and the kind of character and emotional control that enables him to live with large groups of people and work with them cooperatively. The creation of homo sapiens required an evolutionary process slowly selecting for qualities that had survival value in changing environments. At each stage, the best adapted brain made possible the survival of a greater number of descendants. The brain of modern man differs most from that of his primitive ancestors in just those areas in which are lodged the capacity for language, for technical skills, and for certain types of memory.

Toward the end of the stone age, about ten thousand years ago, Homo sapiens numbered perhaps five million head. It had taken him from half a million to a million years to reach such numbers, and to attain those qualities which made him indeed "The Paragon of Animals." The individuals in this large and widely scattered group were on the whole similar in those qualities which most distinguished them from their remote ancestors. But there were physical differences between groups living in different, widely separated areas, and many of these differences were due to variations in their heredity. They differed in color, height, in form of face, and shape of body and limb, and because of these differences they came to be classified in groups, as *races*. Fundamentally, the division of men into the major racial groups came about through mutations and natural selection in particular environments which favored particular traits of mind or body. But in all of the primitive environments hereditary factors for intelligence, adaptability, and various traits of character were essential for survival, and there is no evidence that selection for these traits was any less rigorous in one race than in another.

Within every racial group individuals and families have always varied in their capacity for intelligence, in the quality of their intelligence, in the direction of their interests, and in all the various possibilities of character and motivation. That part of the differences between individuals that derives from variations in heredity is the result of selection within the myriad of environments in which individuals found themselves at one time or another during the long period of human evolution. These environments include not only the physical environments, but all the various social environments in which men succeeded, or failed to survive; the environments of one or another family or tribe, and also the individual niches of the environment within each of the larger classifications in which individual man found his place or failed to find it. The genetic factors that played a part in these small but highly important variations were scattered among the individuals in succeeding generations and became part of the racial heritage of man.

There has never been for long a complete isolation of any human group or race. There has always been intermingling at the borders or as a result of migrations, as clearly shown by the wide distribution among the various races of genetic "markers" such as the blood groups. Caste has sometimes separated the blood lines of intermingled people for long periods of time, but never permanently. Thus there is an almost infinite variety of differences between individuals. Many of these differences, even the small ones, may be extremely important for success in one or another of many particular environments. This little recognized aspect of our inheritance from primitive man, this variety of individual differences, made it possible for man to survive in many environments that would have brought extinction to a less variable species.

There are no records of differential births or deaths of different types of people during the long millennia of prehistory, or of mate selection or of age at marriage. Our positive evidence for the processes of evolution is in the final product, man as he is today, in all his genetic variety. In accounting for this extraordinary end result, we must recognize that nature made her selection of who was to survive not according to any theory of heredity, but in a wholly practical way. Nature admitted as heirs to the future those whose qualities enabled them to survive in the greatest number, without considering the extent to which these qualities were the result of heredity or of environmental influences. Thus culture and tradition both had a role in survival. Man's genetic potential changed in response to the demands of his more complex environment. His capacity for developing intelligence grew manifold; he developed qualities of cooperation and good will beyond those of his apelike ancestors; his personal aggressiveness was modified. Man as we know him today is the product of this kind of interaction between heredity and environment. This is something to bear in mind when we come to consider how man can best help further his own evolution.

◇◇◇◇◇

Survival among Agricultural Peoples
Since 8,000 B.C.

For ten thousand years men have been tilling the soil from fixed abodes. There is no information available on what changes in human types may have taken place in the early part of this period. But for the last two thousand years, when people have been crowded much as they are today, the processes of selection may have been somewhat similar to those taking place a generation ago in the rural districts of China, India, and Pakistan.

A number of studies have been made on agricultural communities in these Asian countries. In 1926 over three hundred Chinese students in schools and colleges were questioned about the size of their families.[3] Where both parents were literate, there had been an average of 6.09 births, and there were 4.24 living children. Where one or both parents were illiterate, there were on the average 5 births and the number of living surviving children was 3.5. In the same study mature women in hospitals were questioned about the size of their families. All of these women were illiterate, but their husbands had varying degrees of education. Those with the more educated husbands had the most children and the most surviving children. The number in this study was small and may not have been representative; but like a number of other studies of the sort, it shows a slightly higher rate of survival among the more educated couples.

A larger and more carefully designed study was made in China in 1929, 1930, and 1931, in the course of a land utilization survey covering a large number of farms that were rated according to size.[4] Questions as to number of children ever born were asked of more than ten thousand women over forty-five years of age. The women on the small farms had borne an average of 5.03 children, and those on the largest farms an average of 5.51 children, the number of children rising step by step with each increase in size of farm. No figures were obtained on number of deaths, but it would be natural to expect a somewhat higher death rate on the smaller farms than on the larger ones. If this was so, then the rate of survival on the small farms was substantially lower than on the large farms.

In India, since 1930 there have been a number of studies of differences in fertility between different socioeconomic classes. In general they show only small differences between classes in number of births, but when mortality is taken into account, the number of surviving children is substantially greater for the more educated and better-off families than for the poorer ones. The most substantial study of this sort was made in Central India by Driver in 1958.[5] India was just beginning to change. This study is probably the last that will give a fair indication of differential fertility in an agricultural community little touched by modern influences. At the time of the study only 5.5% of the couples interviewed "ever" used contraception, and since only the older methods were available at that time, their use was probably not very effective. Conducted by competently trained people using accepted interview methods, the study can be given considerable weight. At the time India still had a high rate of child mortality—a little over 37% for the average of all children born in the interview group.

There were large differences in child mortality by education and economic status of the parents. By the education of the husband, child mortality was 40.4% for husbands with no education, 40% for men with primary education, 34.9% for those with middle school education, over 23% for those with high school and matriculation, and 27.5% for those who had gone through college. For the wives, the story was the same; child mortality was 39.1% for wives with no education, 34% for wives with primary school education, and 23.7% for wives with college education. By land ownership, the couples with the least land had lost 1.8 children, a child mortality of over 40%, and the couples with the most land, twenty or more acres, had lost an average of 1.4 children, a child mortality of 29.2%. Such differences would have a large effect on selection, especially when, as in this time and area, differences in birth rates were smaller and generally favored the better educated and those with larger farms.

In Pakistan, a medical research project begun in 1961 has provided information on the number of living children per couple ranked by education and by income.[6] The study was carried out in and about Lulliani, a small town in the province of Lahore, West Pakistan. A government health center had been recently established, but the habits of the people had not yet noticeably changed. Of the 12,500 people in Lulliani, 33% lived on farms, and the rest were small craftsmen, laborers, shopkeepers, and a few (4%) government personnel. Fifteen percent of the people could read and 12% had had a primary education or better.

Birth rates ranged between 48 and 50 per thousand of population during the period of the study. The number of living children per family varied widely by income and education. Couples in the highest of five income groups averaged 3.23 living children, while couples in the lowest income groups averaged 2.75 living children. The median number of children among illiterates was 2.9, while the median for couples with a primary education or better was 3.4.[7] Among those couples all of whom were illiterate, the median number of living children was 1.9 in the lower income group as compared with 3.0 for the upper income group.

This recent study in Pakistan confirms the results of earlier studies in China and in India. In the villages and farms of these densely crowded areas of Asia, where conditions have changed little in thousands of years, the people who have the larger incomes apparently have more surviving children than those with smaller incomes and the better-educated people have more surviving children than the illiterate. Since literacy and higher incomes are among the rewards of success in agriculture as in other activities, it is fair to say that on the whole the more successful family lines probably survived in greater numbers than the less successful. But differences in education or income do not necessarily imply corresponding differences in hereditary qualities. We can only hazard the guess that there are genetic factors that make some contribution to success in agriculture. If this is so, then there was in these populations a selection favoring those family strains whose genetic quality gave them natural advantages for success in agriculture and village activities.

There is thus some justification for believing that the

forward evolution of man continued among agricultural peoples prior to the Industrial Revolution, the processes of selection being directed not to the survival of primitive hunters, but to meeting the requirements of the agricultural and small-village environment.

2

The United States, 1865-1965 Survival of Family Lines in an Industrialized Modern State

◇◇◇

The Spread of Birth Control and its Effect on Survival.

In the past hundred years, slowly at first, and now at a cumulative rate, birth control has become an accepted pattern of behavior. Together with the development of improved methods of contraception, the increased use of birth control has altogether changed the processes of selection. The effect is all the greater because, during the same period, the death rate has gone down to the point where it no longer has much influence on selection for qualities of mind and character. A hundred years ago over a third of all children died before reaching maturity; today more than 97% live beyond their thirtieth year. In the modern welfare state, children, once they are born, survive in about the same proportion whether their parents are intelligent or stupid, whether they give them adequate or inadequate care. Selection for man's higher qualities must operate almost entirely through differential births, and births are now increasingly coming under conscious individual control.

Until quite recently most people felt that conception was an expression of God's will. For religious people the matter was out of their hands. They could try to avoid death, but except by postponing marriage they could not avoid childbearing. Some tried to limit births by limiting intercourse. Some women, desperate at the thought of having another child to care for, turned to abortion with all its physical and emotional dangers.

Then, toward the end of the nineteenth century, the people of the United States began in increasing numbers to accept the idea of contraception. In the face of public disapproval, over the protests of almost all the churches, in many states in spite of the law, the idea spread that it was proper to prevent conception by some of the means then available. At first it was difficult to get information on contraceptive methods. None of the methods was wholly reliable, and the best were too expensive or too much trouble for people at marginal levels of living. So it was natural that contraception was first used by the more educated and better off, and spread slowly among the less educated and less well off. Even in 1960, when 87% of American married women reported that they used some form of contraception before the end of their reproductive period, it was having little effect on the birth rate of many people on relief or otherwise handicapped in caring for their children. How the idea of contraception spread in the face of so many obstacles is a fascinating story of how, when new problems arise, new ways are found to meet them. There were great pioneers in the movement for birth control: Mrs. Besant in England, Mrs. Sanger in the United States, and many others. They suffered bitter attacks, were publicly insulted and derided, and were many times put in jail. But the cause triumphed, moving slowly at first, and then very rapidly at the end.

For a long time birth control was a matter that could not be discussed politically. It was taboo, for example, in the United Nations. In Latin America until recently any talk of birth control was out of the question. In 1954 the Commissioner of Health of one of our great cities, asked by the Indian Government to advise on a five-year plan for birth control, had to pose as being on a "public health mission" for fear that going over on a birth control mission would be politically dangerous. As recently as 1959 President Eisenhower said: "I cannot imagine anything more emphatically a subject that is not a proper political or governmental activity or function or responsibility. . . ." "This government will not . . . as long as I am here, have a positive political doc-

21

trine in its program that has to do with the problem of birth control. That's not our business." [1] Yet by 1964 Eisenhower and Harry S. Truman had both accepted Honorary Chairmanships of the Planned Parenthood Federation; city-supported hospitals were providing contraceptive advice and services at public clinics, the federal government was helping foreign countries with their programs for limiting births, birth control was openly discussed in the United Nations, and even in South America research programs were going on with the approval of the church. At the same time new methods of birth control were being developed; the "pill" which, taken twenty days each month, prevents ovulation; and the intrauterine contraceptive device, or plastic loop, which is in effect an easily reversible form of sterilization.

For those using such methods, conception is a matter to be planned in advance as an affirmative act; in order to conceive, a woman would have to have the plastic loop removed or stop taking the pill. With the older methods, action to prevent conception had to be taken at a time of emotional excitement. Nor are the pill and the IUDs the final word in birth control. New methods are being developed in research laboratories of government agencies, in medical schools, and in the commercial pharmaceutical companies. These will no doubt hasten and confirm the changes we now see taking place.

Human societies all over the world are in this process of change from the old form of natural selection to the new era of individual selection. The change is most advanced in

North America, Europe, and Japan, but even in these areas it is far from complete. Many couples still have no access to birth control information or services. A large number, probably more than a majority, do not practice birth control effectively. A small proportion of people in every country have only the number of children they have planned for; at the other extreme, a certain proportion exercise no control over the size of their families. In between are the larger number of couples who use contraception more or less effectively and have more or fewer children than they planned for, but eventually limit the size of their families way below the number that would be biologically possible.

Most great social changes are slow in getting started and at some point go on at a cumulative rate. This is the case with the change to contraception. It is being hastened by the improved means of communication between the world's people, and by concern over the too rapid growth of population. Today the governments of half the people in the world are carrying on active campaigns for the control of fertility.

During the period of change, when changing proportions of people are practicing birth control with varying degrees of success, some part of the selective process is due to the old forces of natural selection, and some part is due to the new forces of selection which also are carried out quite unconsciously by the individuals concerned. The two forms are quite different. One kind results from failure of particular types to survive, due mostly to a heavy mortality. The other results almost entirely from differences in size of family, as determined by individuals who are thinking of their personal interests. They will be influenced by their social, psychological, and economic environments, to which people of different heredity will react each in a different way.

Many theories have been put forward about the effects of urbanization, industrialization, and the welfare state on the number and distribution of births, but they are not yet supported by adequate studies. Whatever the influence of these and other factors, the actual change in birth rates is implemented by contraception. This is the finding of all the careful scientific studies that have been made in the past thirty years. The change to contraception has been gradual and is not yet complete. Our information about the present distribution of births in the United States must be, therefore, viewed in this light.

◇◇◇◇◇

Group Differentials in Births; Their Expansion and Decline Over the Past Hundred Years.

Birth control in the United States spread first among our more educated and well-to-do people. For this reason there was, until quite recently, an inverse relation between size of family and education or socioeconomic class. Couples with a college education had smaller families than couples with a high school education. High school couples had fewer children than couples with no more than a grade school education. At all income or occupational levels there was the same inverse relationship: the larger the income and the higher the occupational level, the smaller the family. With every decline in income and level of occupation, size of family went up. When people were classified by intelligence tests there was the same inverse relationship of births to intelligence. It was generally believed by propagandists for eugenics and indeed by many scientists that this sort of a distribution of births was a concomitant of civilization and must make for the deterioration of the human race. Recent studies in the distribution of births and in psychology and behavioral genetics throw doubt on such a generalization.

Births are a variable that changes with conditions. Annual birth rates, that is, births per thousand women per year, may vary from year to year. People are apt to postpone having a child when times are bad. For five years of the great Depression of the thirties the birth rate dropped to an all-time low, and the women of the United States had barely enough children to replace their own number in the next generation. In 1939 there were 2,466,000 births in the United States. Then, as times got better with the War, births went up to about three million at the end of the War, to 3,800,000 in 1947, and to 4,308,000 in 1957. Differences in births between social or educational classes may vary over short periods of time. Couples who were graduates of college and high school were having families of less than two children during the

1930's, not enough to replace their own number in the next generation. But in the 1940's college and high school people were averaging about three children, 30% more than were needed for replacement.[2]

In our discussion of survival in the welfare state we will make little mention of deaths. Over 97% of all children born in the United States today survive to their thirtieth year. Most of the early deaths take place during the first year of life and tend to reduce the survival of defects and deficiencies. Infant mortality in the United States was 25.5 per thousand during the period 1960–62. Group differences in infant mortality were large, as, for instance, rates of 22.6 for whites and 41.8 for nonwhites during this period.[3] But at such low levels even these differences in mortality contribute only 2% to the differential survival of the groups, while differences in births may exceed 50 or 100%.

The reduction in births is not the result of any physiological change. The women of the United States are probably as able to have large families as any women at any time in human history. Indeed, because many of them are descended from pioneers whose losses at childbirth were exceptionally high due to the harsh conditions of frontier life, American women have been through a process of selection for this capacity more severe than that experienced by their European sisters. Improvements in nutrition, medical care, and the control of disease are too recent for relaxed selection to have introduced any great changes in the capacity for successful childbearing. All current studies indicate that American women today could, if they wished, have as many as the average of eight children born to married women in Colonial days, a rate currently being recorded by the Hutterites on this continent [4] and almost achieved today by some groups in the Arab countries.[5] But American women do not want to have so many children. According to a study of a sample of the total United States population made in 1957,[6] on the average, the married women of the United States today want and expect to have about three children. They control the number of their children by contraception, abortion, late marriage, and various forms of restraint. In the United States, contraception is the most important factor in reducing births, and after that, abortion. Most abortions are illegal and there are no reliable figures on their number. Estimates vary from 200,000 to as high as 1,200,000 per year,[7] while the total of births in the United States today is over four million annually. But as there might be nine or ten million births a year if there were no birth control, we must credit contraception with preventing an extra four or five million births a years, a number which would eat us out of house and home in a couple of generations. (People who are opposed to contraception might bear this in mind.)

There are no reliable figures on the early use of birth control in the United States, and we must turn to England for a suggestion of what probably went on here. In 1946 the Royal Commission reported that 15% of English women married before 1910 had used a method of family limitation during their married life. The following table gives the percentages for subsequent years: [8]

YEAR MARRIED	PERCENT OF ENGLISH WOMEN USING CONTRACEPTION
Before 1910	15%
1910–1919	40%
1920–1924	58%
1925–1929	61%
1930–1934	63%
1935–1939	66%

In the United States in 1955, 92% of all fecund couples married fifteen years or more used some form of contraception.[9]

The pattern of family limitations began in the industrialized areas of the northeastern United States early in the nineteenth century. By 1900 birth control was quite generally practiced throughout New England. It spread rapidly through the South Atlantic and Gulf states from 1900 to 1930, and somewhat more slowly through the rest of the country.[10] Its use was greatest among the more educated groups, thus accentuating class differentials in births. The widest differentials in the United States were reached during the great Depression of the thirties. Among the women born between 1901 and 1915, much of whose childbearing years were passed during the Depression, the women at the high school and college level averaged less than two children apiece. At the lower educational levels contraception was not generally in use, and even the pressure of the Depression did not prevent couples with less than an eighth grade education from averaging well over three children, as shown in Table I.

The period of prosperity that came in with World War II brought a sudden rise in the birth rate, and the rise was greatest among the more educated people who had been using contraception most effectively during the Depression. College women born in the five years 1926 through 1930 averaged 2.74 children, as compared to an average of 1.43 for college women born from 1901 through 1905. High school women averaged 2.9 children during the postwar baby boom as compared to 1.8 during the Depression. At the lower educational levels the rise was smaller, as shown in Table I.[11]

Table I: Estimated number of children born per 1,000 white women by the end of childbearing period, for ever-married white women by educational attainment, cohorts of 1901–05 to 1926–1930. (partly estimated)

EDUCATIONAL ATTAINMENT	COHORT GROUP			
	1901–1905	1906–1915	1916–1925	1926–1930
Total	2,456	2,341	2,631	3,018
Less than 8th grade	3,422	3,235	3,418	3,743
8th grade	2,643	2,595	2,879	3,262
High school, 1–3 yrs.	2,290	2,303	2,680	3,085
High school, 4 yrs.	1,818	1,921	2,442	2,919
College, 1–3 yrs.	1,698	1,860	2,439	3,001
College, 4 yrs.	1,434	1,872	2,314	2,745

Based on data on average number of children ever born, from the 1950–1960 Census. Cohort groups estimated by Pascal K. Whelpton.

Extreme differences in size of family between couples at the upper and those at the lower levels of education or of income seem to be a temporary phenomenon of the transition from a time when there was no general use of contraception to the approaching period of its acceptance and use throughout the whole population. By 1960 the differentials were small. In studies made on couples, all of whom used contraception effectively, the differentials were actually reversed, that is, the more intelligent, as measured by intelligence tests, had more children than those with lower IQs.[12]

Most demographers believe that class differentials will soon level off entirely or actually become positive. This is indicated by present trends and by the analysis of unwanted pregnancies made in the recent study of a national sample of women in the United States in 1955.[13] When married couples were asked whether one or both had not wanted their last pregnancy, then or ever, 7% of the college couples said they had not wanted the pregnancy; 9% of the high school graduates had not wanted it; the pregnancy was unwanted by 14% of those with one to three years of high school; it was unwanted by 20% of couples of whom one had gone beyond grade school and one had been only to grade school; and by 33% of couples where both had gone only to grade school.[13] If unwanted pregnancies had not occurred, the better educated would probably have had the largest proportion of children. Recent improvements in contraceptive methods and the continuing trend toward their greater use in all classes makes this a likely prospect.

The trends considered above relate to married couples, and in some cases only to fertile married couples. In two recent studies account has been taken of the proportion unmarried at each economic or educational level, and the proportion of sterility at each level.[14-15] These studies indicate that when unmarried brothers and sisters are taken into account, the survival of family lines is much diminished at the lowest economic and educational levels. Both studies are on small groups of people, and the results may not apply generally. But they suggest that the high negative differentials reported since 1930 may have been somewhat misleading. It is even possible that by 1960 differentials were already favorable to the survival of the groups at the higher levels of education. The best demographic opinion is that this change to favorable birth differentials between large groups classified by education or by income will take place in the near future in the United States, if indeed it has not already happened.

We must not take for granted that a selection favoring the classes that are above the average in education, occupation, or income levels carries any guarantee that the genetic qualities of the race are improving. This question will be discussed in Chapter 13. We can, however, be sure that favorable class differentials will improve certain aspects of our social inheritance. Parents who themselves are well educated are more likely than others to give their children a good education; and a disproportionate increase in the least educated groups in the country is certainly a handicap to the improvement of education from one generation to another.

We must also keep in mind that class differentials in births may vary a great deal over very short periods; they may be affected by differential use of birth control, by differential reaction to economic depressions or good times, by changes in the rate of mobility from one class or occupation to another, and by many other conditions of the environment. Differences in religion, in aspirations, and in training may affect group differences in births. All these things are factors in the social environment which can be, to a greater or less extent, under social control. They may have a favorable or an unfavorable effect on the survival of different kinds of people, regardless of whether social classes are different because of their genetic makeup or because of their environment. Group differentials in births are certainly important to those who would like to see a larger proportion of our children brought up in homes at the higher educational levels. Whether they are also important to improvement in hereditary potential depends on how births are distributed among different kinds of people *within each group.*

◇◇◇◇◇

Birth Differentials between Different Types of Individuals.

For a long time the survival of different types of individuals was confused with the relative survival rate of the different socioeconomic groups. Because the early studies indicated that the least educated classes were having the most children, many people believed that the abler individuals were not reproducing themselves and that society must be in a process of genetic deterioration. Such an unhappy conclusion is not supported by recent studies that use objective measurements applied to individual family lines within the various socioeconomic groupings.

The most widely used objective measure of individual ability is the IQ or Intelligence Quotient. In effect it is a measure of the individual's success in learning in a particular environment. It is thus affected by individual differences in environment as well as by individual differences in heredity. The relation of heredity to IQ will be discussed in Chapter 3. Because of the environmental element, the IQ has a high correlation with education and social class. But it is also to some degree a measure of the individual rather than of the class to which he belongs, because a wide variety of IQs are found in every class. The IQ rating has a high correlation with success in later life. When it is used to compare individuals in a group of people brought up in a similar environment, differences in the IQ of individuals in the group may be considered to reflect differences in their heredity; when it is used to compare the two members of identical twin pairs reared apart in different environments, differences in IQ reflect differences in their environments.

A study reported in 1962 [16] was made on some 85,000 persons living in Minnesota, all of whom were descendants of the grandfathers of 300 patients in a state mental institution whose family records had been carefully recorded. The study covered two generations. IQs were obtained from the Minnesota school system and other sources. Included in the study were all the unmarried brothers and sisters. When they were counted in, it was found that the family lines with IQs of 131 and above had produced an average of 2.96 children, far more than the family lines with IQ levels below 56, and somewhat above the size of family of those with IQs 56 to 85, while those with the intermediate IQs between 71 and 130 averaged substantially smaller families, with a positive relationship between IQ and number of children. When the survival rates at different IQ levels are balanced out, the study shows no evidence for changes in average IQ from one generation to the next in this group of 1,016 families. No record was made of the use of birth control. It is probable that during this period prior to the end of World War II, there was little effective use of contraception among the lower IQ individuals in the study. Under today's conditions, with improved and more widely used methods of contraception, we would expect that size of family at the lower educational levels would be substantially reduced.

Another large study was made on 1,144 native white Protestant individuals, most of them urban born in 1916 or 1917, who had been tested in the sixth grade by the Kalamazoo, Michigan, school system.[17] When the study was made in 1961–62, they were about forty-five years old, and childbearing had been completed with an average of 2.24 children per individual, a normal number for the period of the great Depression that prevailed during their early married lives. Like the subjects of the Minnesota study, the individuals at the lower educational levels in the Michigan study were probably not yet making much use of birth control, while those at the upper educational levels were using birth control and having smaller families than ever before, far smaller than comparable couples were having ten years later. In contrast to the Minnesota study, the marriage rate was high at all levels of IQ, but of those with the lowest IQ, twice as many were childless as those with the highest IQs.

In the Michigan study, including the unmarried and the childless, those with an IQ of 130 and over averaged 3 children; those with an IQ of 71 to 85 averaged 2.3 children, and those with an IQ below 70 had no children. A comparison of the findings of this study and of the Minnesota study is shown in Table II.

Both of these studies are limited in that they include only a relatively small number of people in areas where class differences may be smaller than in most parts of the country. But they agree in the finding that individual family lines of high intelligence seem to be far from dying out at the present time. Both agree in the finding that individuals just above subnormal intelligence have larger than average families. Both agree that subnormal individuals at the lowest levels of intelligence have a low fertility.

This bimodal relationship of fertility to IQ, in which more than average fertility is found among the highest and again among the next to lowest IQ individuals, is probably a recent development.

The changing nature of these relationships is shown by

Table II: Comparison of the results of Michigan study with those of Minnesota study

| | MINNESOTA STUDY * HIGGINS AND REED (1962) | | MICHIGAN STUDY BAJEMA (1963) | |
IQ RANGE	NO. OF INDIVIDUALS	AVG. NO. OFFSPRING	NO. OF INDIVIDUALS	AVG. NO. OFFSPRING
>130	25	2.96	23	3.00
116–130	269	2.45	107	2.57
101–115	778	2.26	344	2.08
86–100	583	2.16	427	2.30
71–85	208	2.39	75	2.05
56–70	74	2.46	3	0.00
0–55	29	1.38	0	0.00

* NOTE: The large proportion of low IQ's in the Minnesota study may be due to the inclusion of families with relatives in the State Mental Hospital.

figures from the U.S. census on the size of family of American women according to their attained education. (Years of education is not, of course, the same thing as IQ, but the two have a considerable correlation.) As the childbearing period of American women moved from the Depression of the thirties to the prosperity of the postwar period, the birth rate went up at all levels of education; but the rise was least at the lower levels of education and greatest for those who went to college (see Table I, p. 29). Over the twenty-five year period, those with less than an eighth grade education showed an increase in size of family from an average of 3.4 to an average of 3.7.

Those with a college education showed an increase in number of children from 1.4 to an average of 2.7 children.[18] If there is another depression, differences in the use of birth control will undoubtedly be much less than they were in the thirties, and the large group differentials of that period would probably not be repeated.

The relation of size of family to success in life has been changing over the past generation, as evidenced by the number of children of people listed in *Who's Who* at different times. Men currently in *Who's Who* have had about enough children to replace themselves, and the younger men who have not yet completed their families may equal or exceed the national average family size for their age groups.[19] This is in considerable contrast to the men listed in *Who's Who* in 1926–27 who, taking into account those unmarried as well as married, had fewer children than the number needed for replacement, and far fewer than the number in the general population at that time of relatively high birth rates.[20]

An early trend toward larger families among the more successful college graduates appears in three studies made before World War II. In 1927 studies were made of size of family of Harvard and Yale graduates as related to their "success" in life, and a similar study was made on Princeton graduates in 1938. In the Harvard and Yale studies, sucess was determined by the judgment of classmates. In the Princeton study only the "businessmen" were rated for sucess, and the ratings were based on their financial success. The results are shown in Table III.

Table III: Fertility Differentials among graduates of Harvard, Princeton, and Yale

		NO. OF CASES	PERCENT MARRIED	AV. NO. CHILDREN PER MAN	AV. NO. CHILDREN PER MAR-RIED MAN	PERCENT CHILDLESS COUPLES
HARVARD MEN [*]						
Most successful	(1)	120	93	2.02	2.17	19
	(2)	430	87	1.76	2.05	18
	(3)	735	87	1.54	1.78	23
	(4)	473	72	1.03	1.43	36
Least successful	(5)	131	58	0.74	1.28	38
PRINCETON MEN [†]						
Most successful businessmen	(1)	338	93.	1.97 [a]	2.14	15.7
Moderate	(2)	366	86.7	1.56	1.80	18.9
Least successful businessmen [b]	(3)	54	66.8	1.09	1.64	22.2
YALE MEN [‡]						
Most successful	(1)	140	92.85	2.27	2.44	17.69
	(2)	139	85.70	1.78	2.08	16.80
	(3)	138	83.35	1.63	1.95	20
	(4)	138	83.35	1.33	1.60	32.17
Least successful	(5)	137	66.45	.86	1.29	48.66

[a] Standard error — .064 Fisher's test applied to the difference between the mean number of children per man for the most successful businessmen, and for the mean of all Princeton men shows a probability of the difference being due to chance alone of less than one in several hundred, so the difference may be considered significant.

[b] Unpublished data supplied by J. J. Osborn.

[*] John C. Phillips, Success and the birth rate; *Harvard Graduates' Magazine*, 1927, pp. 565–570.

[†] John J. Osborn, Fertility differentials among Princeton alumni, *J. Heredity*, December 1939, pp. 565–567.

[‡] Ellsworth Huntington and Leon Whitney, Unpublished material used as basis of chart in *The Builders of America* by Huntington and Whitney, William Morrow & Co, Inc., 1927.

The "most successful" college men averaged about two children apiece, and the "least successful" about one child apiece. This large difference was partly due to differences in the percentage married, 93% being married among the most successful in each of the colleges, as against 58% to 66% married among the least successful, partly due to the number of children, 2.14 to 2.44 for the successful married graduates as compared to from 1.28 to 1.64 for the least successful married graduates; and partly due to the much greater number of childless couples among the least successful than among the most successful. The three studies showed closely similar results, although the Princeton study was made ten years later than the others, and the criterion of "success" was in one case financial, and in the others, the opinion of classmates. Both criteria reflect the combined influence of heredity and environment.

In Terman's study of "A Thousand Gifted Children" there is a close relation between IQ and success in life. The group consisted of 1,528 children whose IQ placed them in the upper one percent of the school population of the larger California cities. They were selected solely on the basis of their performance on a standard intelligence test, which they took at the average age of eleven years. The group were restudied in 1955, when they averaged forty-five years of age. By all the usual measures of success, such as income and occupational position, they exceeded the average of the general population and of those in similar activities. A larger than average proportion were married by age forty-five and they

39

had at least the average number of children for people in their income class.

With our present limited knowledge we can draw only tentative conclusions about the rates of survival of family lines at different levels of intelligence. It seems likely that from the turn of the century until about 1940, the birth rate and survival rate of the least intelligent individuals was higher than that of the more intelligent individuals. There may have been for a while some decrease in the frequency of genetic factors for high intelligence. Since 1945 it would seem that this tendency has been arrested, and that for twenty years a fair equilibrium has been maintained.

It is hard to forecast future trends in the distribution of births at different levels of intelligence. We can be sure that improved, cheaper, more effective, and more acceptable methods of contraception will be developed. We can expect that they will be made available to people at every level of intelligence, character, and income, so that size of family will become for everyone a matter of personal choice. Contemporary studies such as we have cited above indicate that at the present time, when birth control is generally in use, the more successful people in every environment have the most children. But the margin is not large and such trends in births can change quickly.

3

The Genetic Significance
of Group and Individual Birth
Differentials

◇◇

Measuring the Heredity Component
in Intelligence and Personality.

The possibilities inherent in any individual man or woman are beyond measurement. Each man will, at a particular time in his life, respond to a particular challenge of the environment in his own particular and different way. Predictions of how men may react to given circumstances may be accurate for a large majority of those involved, but there will always be a number whose reaction is highly individual, quite different from that of the majority.

Man's behavior is not the result of heredity alone; it is the result of his heredity as it has been molded by his environment. Each man is, at birth, unique. There is no other man like him. The genetic code for his design differs from the genetic code of every other individual man. His ten thousand or more genes were inherited from millions of ancestors, with random changes throughout this long succession. Even though all men sprang from a common ancestry at the beginning of life, it is inconceivable that any two should have an identical set of genes, with the single exception of identical twins, who derive from the same fertilized cell and are genetically not two individuals, but one.

But even identical twins are not alike. Before their birth they have received different amounts of nutrition, as chance may have given them a favorable or an unfavorable place in their mother's womb, and, though the difference in weight may be made up after birth, the mother may favor the one who was smaller and weaker when she first held them in her arms. Thus what was at first a physical difference in their environment may become a lasting psychological difference in their environment. All through their lives such slight influences will make for differences even between identical twins.

The genetic code lays down only a general design, and leaves much room for the environment to work on the material supplied by the cells. In the development of man's intellectual and emotional qualities the influences of the environment operate over a wide range of possibilities. In this respect man is far more elastic than any of the other higher mammals, or indeed any other form of life. So great is the range of ability affected by different environments that in the past some psychologists have held that differences in heredity played little part in individual differences in intelligence. But more recent studies show that hereditary potentials vary over an equally wide range. We are forced to think in terms of the interdependence of heredity and environment in human development, each varying in a range limited only by the requirements of survival.

The old question, "Which is the more important, heredity or environment?" has little meaning as a generality. It makes sense only when it is applied to a particular characteristic of a particular individual in a particular environment at a particular time. In the extreme case of certain physical defects the environment may count for very little. A mongolian idiot has in every cell in his body an extra chromosome that can actually be seen through a microscope. We can properly say that his defect is due to a variation in his heredity. But if a child is simply mentally retarded, it may either be because of a deprived environment, or because of some emotional stress, or because of a physical injury, or because in his case heredity set a low limit on his mental development, or it may be a combination of all four. At the other extreme, in the case of genius that arises in an apparently poor environment, we must conclude that some unusual combination of superior inherited material has enabled him to reach a level so far above that of his fellows.

There is no way of making a direct measure or assessment

of the design laid down by the genetic code of a particular individual. We can only get a general idea of the design by noting the form it has taken after having been molded by the environment. Because different individuals react differently to the same environment, studies in which the environment is held constant and the heredity varied or studies in which the heredity is held constant (as with identical twins) and the environment varied, give a general indication rather than a specific answer about an individual. Such studies require a measure or test that can be applied to the individual man. Here again there is a difficulty. Physical measurement may be made with a good deal of assurance, but measures of a man's mental or emotional characteristics have meaning only insofar as these qualities can be defined, and this is difficult because of their complexity and variety.

Today the most widely used measure of mental qualities is the intelligence test, usually reported in terms of the Intelligence Quotient, or intelligence as related to age. Intelligence tests are sometimes supplemented by various tests of personality, but these latter are harder to administer and have less established validity. For this reason our discussion of heredity components will be limited to studies using measures of intelligence. There is a high correlation between test intelligence and certain traits of personality, and more often than not, a high IQ seems to go with socially valuable traits of personality and with success in the professions and business.[1]

Psychological tests, including intelligence tests, measure only one ability or constellation of abilities at a time, while an individual's achievement, his capacity to enjoy life, and his social value are not determined by any single psychological characteristic, but by the combination and interaction of his intelligence, his personality, his motivation and attitudes, his physical qualities, and all the other attributes that go to making up the entire man.

Intelligence tests ask questions about what the individual has learned, or they test his reactions, which may be either inherent or learned. When intelligence tests are used with large groups of people from different backgrounds, a single test standardized on people from one environment cannot be expected to provide fair comparisons when applied to people from another environment. Some of the early tests were quite naïve in this respect. For instance, a test standardized on city children might ask the question, "What does it cost to ride in the subway?", which is not a fair question to ask a country child. A test standardized on country children might ask, "Which end of a cow gets up first?", to which any intelligent country child would answer, "The rear end, of course," while most city children would not know the answer. Even the sophisticated tests in use today are at their best when they are used to compare individuals in a group which has a generally similar background. The more similar the environment, the more valid the comparison as a measure of hereditary differences between the individuals in the group.

Intelligence tests also measure the factor of heredity when they are used to compare the intra-pair differences in intelligence between identical twins reared together and those reared apart, or the differences between identicals and fraternals, or in comparisons of the intra-pair differences between less related pairs. When identical twins are reared apart, we can make a rough approximation of the differences in their environments and compare their intra-pair differences with those of identical twins reared together in approximately similar environments. Or we can compare the intra-pair differences between identical twins with those between brothers and sisters, or between quite unrelated pairs. Such studies have been made. They point conclusively to both heredity and environment as factors in individual differences.[2]

Identical twins reared together in the same home are remarkably alike. They usually do not differ in test intelligence much more than the same individual differs on intelligence tests given him on different days. But fraternal twins reared together are no more alike than any two brothers or sisters. The genetic codes of a pair of identical twins carry identical designs, but long before birth, and all through their lives, the structure dictated by the design is molded by the environment in which it grows and changes. When identical twins are reared apart, they develop substantial differences in intelligence level, always in the direction of the stimulus afforded them by their environments. But even when they are reared apart, their average differences are no greater than the average differences between fraternal twins reared together, and much smaller than the differences between ordinary brothers and sisters or between unrelated pairs.[3]

In other studies the similarity of intelligence between

46

adopted children and their foster parents has been compared to the similarity of natural children and their true parents. Even after taking into account factors that might produce a bias, such as selective placement of the children in their foster homes, it is clear that when the children are matched, factor for factor, with the exception of a biological tie to their parents, there is a closer resemblance in intelligence between children and their true parents than there is between adopted children and their foster parents.[4]

When identicals are reared apart, their differences are evidently due to differences in their environments. When unrelated pairs of children brought up in the same home differ more than related pairs, the differences may be accounted for by their different heredities. Such studies indicate that both differences in heredity and differences in the environment play a part in determining differences in intelligence as measured by intelligence tests. The proportion of the difference contributed by heredity and the proportion contributed by the environment can only be determined for individual cases and in respect to their particular circumstances.

Differences in hereditary capacity for intelligence between large social or racial groups are hard to measure because, in the case of groups, neither heredity nor environment can be held constant. A group is composed of a great number of individuals, each reacting in a different way to different environments. We cannot speak of the intelligence of a group of people, but only of the average intelligence of all the individuals in the group. If we measure the individuals in any group and place them on a chart by levels of intelligence, we find that they lie along what the statistician calls a "normal curve of distribution." The mass cluster around the midpoint of intelligence, and the very intelligent and the very unintelligent lie on either side.

Any other group, living perhaps under very different environmental conditions, would also find its members distributed along a normal curve, but with the midpoint of the curve at perhaps a quite different point in the scale of intelligence. This can be illustrated by the charts taken from N. D. Hirsch's [5] study made in 1928, comparing two thousand East Kentucky mountain children with a similar number of urban children. The urban children had on the average a far higher IQ than the mountain children, which was natural since the intelligence tests were easier for the urban children to understand than for the mountain children. Even though this is an old study, using methods less sophisticated than those in use today, it is valuable as an example because these groups differed in IQ more than such groups would differ today, and yet there was a large overlapping of their curves of distribution. A substantial proportion of the urban children were more stupid than the average of the mountain children. The chart clearly shows this overlapping.

The overlapping shown in the chart illustrates two aspects of group differences which must always be borne in mind by anyone considering eugenic problems. The first is the almost universal existence of an overlap, whatever quality the group is being measured for. For example, Appalachian mountaineers

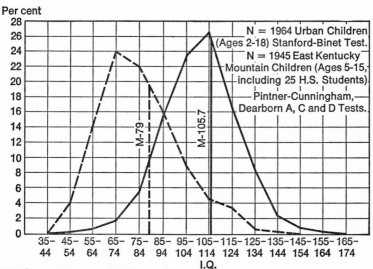

*Distribution of Scores on Intelligence Tests
Made by American Urban and East Kentucky Mountain School Children.*

are taller than recent immigrants to the United States; but if the two groups are put on a chart, their curves of distribution overlap: many of the mountaineers are shorter than the average of the immigrants, many of the immigrants taller than the average of the mountaineers. One can only say that the average of a group shows a quality different from the average of some other group. Only the individuals exhibit the quality.

The overlap shown on the chart may also have quite another significance. Being classified as these groups were, by the environment in which they were brought up, does not mean that all the mountaineers had the same rural environ-

49

ment, and all the city children the same urban environment. In each case the environments must have differed over a wide range. Some of the mountaineers undoubtedly had better schooling than some of the urban children; some of the city children may have had poorer schooling than the average of the mountaineers. Part of the differences shown in the chart may have been due simply to variations in the environmental stimulus within each group. The study is a good example of the hazards involved in trying to interpret the meaning of group comparisons in intelligence.

Many misconceptions about race have developed through failure to recognize the limitations of intelligence tests, particularly when they are used for comparisons between two different groups. The environment of the Negro in the United States is everywhere so different from the environment of the white man that differences in response to an intelligence test cannot be taken as indicating differences between the two races in hereditary capacity for intelligence. Intelligence tests given to all recruits in World War I provided an anomaly that greatly distressed many people who had been writing about race inferiorities. When the test intelligence of Negroes was compared with the test intelligence of whites from the same locality, the average for the white man was always superior to the average of the Negroes. But the Negro recruits in five northern states were superior in their response to intelligence tests to the white recruits in eight south-central states.[7] Various interpretations were given at the time, but today it is generally agreed that the northern Negroes tested higher because the northern urban environment was more stimulating than the southern environment, particularly with respect to the kind of questions used in the Army tests.

Intelligence tests are not in general a direct measure of hereditary endowment. But there is a clear correlation between comparative success in intelligence tests and comparative success or achievement in life within groups of people who have had similar or comparable educational opportunities.[8] Those individuals who give the best response to intelligence tests are, in general, above the average of their group in success or achievement. To the extent that there is a correlation between intelligence and success within the group, intelligence tests are a valuable measure for use in studies of the survival of family lines at varying levels of hereditary endowment.

There are of course many other measures of comparative "success." Where educational opportunities are similar, classroom standing is a fair measure of comparative success. A person's success in life can be measured in terms of the individual's achievement compared to that of others with similar opportunities in the same field; it can be measured by various objective means, or by the judgment of peers, or by the judgment of posterity. Winning a Nobel prize, or inclusion in *Who's Who in America,* may be a mark of success for a professional man. The athlete may be termed successful if he is the choice for an all-American team, or wins a championship, or is in the Baseball Hall of Fame; the musician if he leads one of the great orchestras; the author if he sells many books; the executive by the size of the company he heads; the businessman by the money he makes or the size of his operations. Properly used, and allowing for inherited position and other exceptions, money earnings are a measure of success which can be applied to the great majority of working people in whatever occupation, so long as the comparisons are made within each occupation; though allowance must be made for those who are in occupations which are not appropriate to their genetic dispositions. Money earnings are most effective as a measure of native ability when they are used in a mobile society, where men can find the job for which each is best fitted.

Francis Galton, the father of eugenics, wrote, "There can hardly be a better evidence of a person being adapted to his circumstances than that afforded by success." [9] The yardstick of success in life in his particular environment is a measure of the whole man, of the combination of all his attributes and their effectiveness in manipulating his environment. In the long period of human evolution success in his physical environment meant his survival and that of his children; success in his social environment often meant his having many wives and many children. Often then, as now, success and survival depended partly on luck, but out of this kind of success and survival evolution created Homo Sapiens in all his present diversity. Studies of the differential survival of individuals at different levels of success do not show the extent of genetic change, but they do show the general direction of change, since we know that some part of individual differences in achievement depend on variations in genetic factors.

◇◇◇◇◇

The Index of Opportunity for Selection.

Selection can take place only when there are differences in mortality and in number of births. If everyone died at the same age and everyone had the same number of children, there would be no opportunity for selection. Variations between individuals in mortality and number of children create the opportunity for selection to take place.

At first glance it would seem that the opportunity for selection must be reduced in a population in which the married women, instead of having six or eight children, have on the average only three, almost all of whom live to reproduce. But this is not necessarily the case. A formula has been devised for finding out how much room there is for selection to operate under different rates of births and deaths. The formula rests on the assumption that if everyone lived to the end of his reproductive years and everyone had the same number of children, there would be no opportunity for selection; the frequency of each of the different genes in the population would remain the same, except as it might be changed by new mutations and their accumulation. The formula provides an Index of Opportunity for Selection, I, which is the sum of two parts, I_m, the index due to mortality, and I_f, the index due to variations in fertility. The greater the proportion of deaths before the age of reproduction and the greater the variations in fertility, the greater is the opportunity for selection. When deaths before the age of reproduction are reduced, deaths offer a reduced opportunity for selection. But contrary to what one might expect, when births per woman go down, the Index of Opportunity for Selection by differences in fertility does not necessarily decline—it may actually increase. This is because, when the average size of family is smaller, there may be a greater variation in departures from the average. Thus when the average size of family is 2.3 as it was in the great Depression of the thirties, the woman who had seven children had three times the average; but in Colonial times in the United States, when the average was seven or eight, few women had even twice the average.

The formula for fertility, I_f, has been applied to a number of existing populations with the result shown in Table IV.[10]

The index for I_m, mortality, shows more change but less fluctuation. The reduction of mortality since primitive times has changed the index for mortality from about 1, where half the children die before maturity, to an index of less than .03, when less than 3% of the children die before maturity. But this low Index of Opportunity for Selection by Mortality does not signify a corresponding reduction in the actual selection taking place; of the less than 3% of the children who die in the United States before reaching maturity, probably a majority die from some genetic defect or anomaly. Among

Table IV: Index of Opportunity for Selection Due to Variations in Fertility

POPULATION	AVERAGE CHILDREN BORN PER WOMAN	IF
Rural Quebec	9.9	.20
Hutterites, USA	9.0	.17
Gold Coast, Africa	6.5	2.3
Ramah Navajo Indians	2.1	1.57
U.S. women born in 1839	5.5	.23
U.S. women born 1871–75	3.5	.71
U.S. women born in 1909	2.1	.876
U.S. women born in 1928 (not completed)	2.85	.446

primitive people, when at times half the children died, far the greater proportion died from causes having no relation to their genetic constitutions. Today a large proportion of infant deaths are related to hereditary conditions, and even with a low Index of Opportunity for Selection, many of the most serious forms of congenital defect are eliminated by neonatal and prenatal deaths.

The Index of Opportunity for Selection by Fertility may be very variable in periods when fertility is reduced by birth control. As shown in Table IV, the Index of Opportunity for Selection by Fertility, I_f, was .23 for women born in 1839, who had averaged 5.5 children, and was .876, or four times as great, for U.S. women born in 1909, who had averaged only 2.1 children apiece. The high index for the women born in

1909 was due to the large social class differentials in births during the Depression. Differences in the Index, I_f, depend on whether size of family clusters around the average as it did during the fifties, or whether large proportions are found at the extremes, with many small families and many large families, as was the case during the Depression of the thirties.

In any consideration of the changes that may be taking place in genetic characteristics from one generation to another, it is important to remember that there may be large variations in the Index of Opportunity for Selection even in populations with a low death rate and a low average birth rate. It is not the average size of family which matters, but the variations in size of family within the average.

◇◇◇◇◇

Genetic Change Resulting from Group Differentials in Births.

In the early part of this chapter we noted the great difficulty of measuring differences in average hereditary capacity for intelligence between large social or racial groups (p. 47). Groups are composed of individuals, and the standing of a group in intelligence or any other characteristic in which heredity may play a part is the average of all the individuals of which the group is composed. In the same way, group differences in births represent the average number of children born to all the individuals in the group. When all members of a group share a particular hereditary characteristic, such as, for instance, skin color in a racial group, then differentials in births between different groups are important for changes in the proportion of people with that particular characteristic. But when groups are classified by socioeconomic status, place of residence, or race, the individuals in the group may be at many different levels of genetic capacity for a characteristic as complex as intelligence. In the case of such qualities, any group differences in births may be easily offset by differences in the birth rates of individuals within the group. If in such a group the birth rate of individuals who are above average in intelligence falls below the rate needed for replacement, many valuable genes are lost —a loss which society cannot well afford. If the birth rate of individuals with less than average intelligence is above replacement, an excess of "poor" genes will be continued to the detriment of society.

In the case of groups classified by measures in some degree selective for intelligence, as, for instance, those classified as "professional," and used in comparison with groups whose classification is less indicative of intelligence, differentials in births between the groups may be a considerable factor in genetic change. But until we have a more substantial body of evidence than that presently available, we must rest on the assumption that even in such groups, group differentials in births are not as important for genetic change as are differentials between individuals of different genetic potential within each group. And for groups classified by characteristics not directly related to intelligence, group differentials in births have little significance for genetic change. Individual differentials in births are the overriding factor.

. Our discussion has been limited to the subject of intelligence because of the paucity of objective evidence on other psychological traits. The more limited material on personality traits gives some evidence that changes in the genetic aspects of socially valuable traits of personality follow in general the lines indicated for traits of intelligence.

These findings should be taken into account by those people, and there have been many of them in the past, who believe that the road to genetic improvement lies in changing the reproductive habits of whole groups of people classified by their occupations, their level of schooling, their race, or their incomes.

◇◇◇◇◇

Genetic Change as a Result of Differences in Size of Family Between Individuals.

As we have already noted, there are no measures available of "hereditary" qualities of intelligence; there are only measures of developed qualities that are the joint product of heredity and environment. Such measures as the IQ give some indication of hereditary differences in intelligence between individuals who have been brought up in approximately the same educational environment. To this extent, studies of individuals classified by IQ provide the only available evidence of changes in hereditary capacities for developing intelligence that may be taking place from one generation to another. The Minnesota and Kalamazoo, Michigan, studies discussed in Chapter II (pp. 33–36) are unique in that they provide information on the survival of family lines, taking into account the childless or unmarried brothers and sisters of the parents. These studies were made, not on a national sample of the population, but on rather specialized groups; and they provide no way of relating the IQ of the individuals to their particular environment within the group. But each study shows rather similar rates of survival for family lines represented by individuals at various levels of IQ. If these studies can be taken as representative of the population as a whole, there seems to be little change going on in the United States today from one generation to another in the proportion of hereditary factors for different kinds of intelligence.

We cannot, however, conclude from these two studies that the balance of intelligence is going to remain as it is for any length of time. The United States is still in the process of changing from the limited use of birth control practiced in the nineteenth century, to the almost universal use of birth control that may be expected before the end of the twentieth century. To sum up recent trends, in the earlier stages of the change, say, during the 1920's, the evidence indicated a disproportionate increase in the family lines of people of less than average capacity for intelligence. The groups practicing birth control had a lower birth rate than the groups that did not practice birth control, and it is a reasonable inference that within each group there was a similar distribution—fewer births among those in the group who were above the average in capacity for intelligence; more births among those below the average. By 1960 the group differentials had leveled off to a great extent, and the two studies cited indicate that differences within the groups had also leveled off.

One cannot say with any certainty that the change to a more favorable distribution of births will continue with the increasing spread of birth control. Too many other factors may intervene. But we can be sure that the opportunity for a favorable selection will increase as we move toward the complete control of births by individuals at every level of income and education, and with every variety of hereditary capacity for intelligence. Not long ago college graduates were having only half as many children as people with only a grade school education. Now college graduates, selected for their intelligence more than in the past, are having almost as many children as graduates of grade schools. It is possible that in the future college graduates, all of them selected for intelligence, might have substantially more children than grade school graduates who had not been bright enough to get to college —the difference being a matter of conscious choice. Or, as seems less likely, the reverse might take place, with a return to the negative differentials of the great Depression of the thirties.

In the case of those physical traits that are determined by relatively simple patterns of inheritance, especially those involving recessive genes, very rapid changes could take place in the frequency of genes for these characteristics. Red hair is determined by recessive genes. If there were no matings except between redheaded people, the whole population would be redheads in a single generation. But with intelligence, personality, and character, we are dealing with traits which are undoubtedly polygenic—the product of a number of genes or constellations of genes. Sometimes these constellations of genes are linked together and inherited as a whole, passing on the trait to the next generation in undiminished vigor. More often they disappear in part, or occur again only occasionally. There is a tendency for the children of bright parents to regress toward the mean of their family stocks. There is the likelihood that high capacities for intelligence may not develop without the particular qualities of personality that made intelligence effective in the parental stock.

We do not know the limits of the change that might take place with the present stock of human genes. In the words of the eminent geneticist Theodosius Dobzhansky, "Human populations contain an ample supply of genetic variability from which selection could construct new adaptive hereditary endowments. The genetic variability having arisen of course by mutations in the past, is sufficient for any conceivable evolutionary engineering that man may decide to undertake. This would require not more mutation, but more selection of the already existing variants." [11] We can be quite certain that, to the extent that the distribution of births was favorable to genetic improvement, there would be an improvement in average capacity for intelligence and the aspects of character associated with it, enabling each new generation to develop and enjoy changed and improved environments with each successive step in the improvement of their heredity.

The present distribution of births in the United States does not appear to be changing our average genetic capacity for intelligence from one generation to another. This is in contrast to the period of the nineteen thirties when indications pointed in general to the likelihood of a decline in genetic capacity; and equally in contrast to the period which is perhaps forecast by present trends, when we might hope for an actual improvement in average genetic capacity for intelligence. Since there would at the same time be an increase in the proportion of children raised by parents at the higher levels of intelligence, and a decrease in the proportion of children raised by parents at the lowest levels of intelligence, the results would be cumulative for both heredity and environment, and of immense importance to the future of man.

4

Defects and Abnormalities

Everyone carries through life a number of genetic weaknesses and deficiencies. Some may be as mild and appear as early as a tendency to flat feet. Some may appear late in life and be as serious as crippling arthritis or senile dementia. Some may be a spur to ambition, but more frequently they are a tragedy to the individual and to his family. Mild or serious, they are a diminution of that perfection to which each one of us aspires. If there were indeed a man without genetic weaknesses or deficiencies, he would be immune to all communicable diseases known to his ancestors; he would have a perfect digestion for every kind of food; chronic illnesses would be unknown to him; he would round out a life span of perhaps a hundred years in full mental vigor, with eyesight unimpaired, with perfect teeth and perfect hearing. In fact, for the rest of us he would be a rather unpleasant fellow to have around.

Has the race deteriorated from an earlier perfection? That was the belief of many early writers, but there is little evidence available to substantiate it. Some comparisons can be made between the structure of primitive men according to their fossil remains, and the structure of civilized man today, or between the frequency of certain genetic defects among relict groups of primitive men still in existence and their frequency among people long living under the conditions of an agricultural civilization. Studies of this sort are not conclusive, but they may give evidence (mostly relating to minor defects) of what happens when the forces of selection are weakened or "relaxed" by an easier environment.

◇◇◇◇◇

Evidence for Relaxed Selection.

Ten thousand years ago when men began a settled agricultural life, the personal dangers of the wandering hunter were replaced by the community dangers of bad crops, famines, and contagious diseases. Selection was relaxed for some of the qualities that must have been important to the survival of primitive man, but other qualities, of little importance to primitive man, became important to survival under the more crowded conditions of farm and village life. We might therefore expect that during these ten thousand years there were substantial changes in the frequency of various types of personal qualities and of the related genes in human populations. This expectation has some confirmation in what we know about domestic animals.

Darwin noted a case of relaxed selection in the loss by domestic ducks of the ability to fly. He called it a case of "biological degeneration." Most domestic animals have suffered diminished efficiency or loss of their ancestor's protective coloring, keenness of sensory perception, various instinctive mechanisms, and many other adaptive traits. Without human aid, considerable numbers of most breeds of domestic fowl and beasts would die at birth, fail to feed during growth, or fall prey to vermin and other predators. Many would even be lacking in capacity for mating. If they were returned to their natural wild habitats where they would have to fend for themselves, it would seem doubtful that many would survive. We accept the "deterioration" because the domesticated breeds are in other respects better adapted to their habitats of enclosed pastures and feed pens than their wild ancestors. In their case the sum total of genetic change is actually advantageous. The application of such a situation to man may not be particularly exact or even relevant, yet it does suggest that human populations with the longest histories of non-hunting culture may have a high frequency of traits that in primitive man would have represented a deterioration.

Probably the best authenticated case of relaxed selection in man is that of the common types of sex-linked deficiencies in color vision, or "colorblindness." At least four types have been defined: deuteranomaly and deuteranopia (mild and severe "green deficiency"), protanomaly and protanopia (mild and severe "red deficiency"). Each is caused by a defect or mutation in one or another genetic locus on the X chromosome; each is subject to relatively facile and reliable diagnosis; each is manifest from childhood, and each is highly impervious to training or to the usual environmental influences throughout life.[1] Studies of population frequencies have shown prevailingly low rates of colorblindness among primitive people still living in hunting and food-collecting cultures, such as Australian aborigines with a rate of 2%, and Fiji Islanders with rates from 0 to .8%. Such rates contrast markedly with the higher rates among populations having the most ancient histories of agriculture. For example, Chinese and Japanese rates vary from 4% to 7%, based on aggregate samples of over 67,000 and 249,000 men, respectively. (Since the genes for these types of colorblindness are sex-linked, the best estimate of gene frequency is the frequency of the trait among males.) Most European and West Asian rates vary from 5% to 10%. In the United States, white servicemen average about 8% colorblind; Negroes between 3% and 4%. It is maintained (though the proof is not yet sufficient) that preagricultural ancestors once had the same low rates as those of contemporary primitive peoples, such as the Fiji Islanders, and that with cultural advance, agriculture and settled village habitats, followed by gradual urbanization, selection against colorblindness has diminished or relaxed.[2]

Another case for relaxed selection may be found in defective vision acuity, which has frequently been reported as less prevalent among "primitive" than among "civilized" populations. But for a number of reasons this case is not as well supported as that of colorblindness. The causes of diminished acuity are complex and variable; the effects of environment are controversial, particularly the extent to which close work and poor lighting during childhood may produce eyestrain and diminished acuity; and little is known about the possible effects of training to produce the remarkably superior acuity reported in certain studies of savages. Furthermore, vision defects result from the interaction of a number of genes, whereas the various forms of sex-linked colorblindness are based on single genes. All these complications must be taken into account, but the fact remains that studies among primitive hunting populations indicate not only lower frequencies of acuity below 20/20 than among large samples of Asians and Europeans, but also, even more impressive, higher frequencies of acuities considerably superior to 20/20. Most cases of lower acuity are due to myopia, the hereditary basis of which is high. That the dichotomy between the high rates among "civilized" populations and the low rates among "savages" is clearer for myopia than for defective vision in general, somewhat strengthens the case for relaxed selection in myopia.[3] Natural selection probably favored mild degrees of myopia in certain primitive cultures for such activities as flint chipping, wood carving, painting, etc. Its higher frequencies today may be due in great part not only to relaxed selection, but also to positive selection for particular environments.

A third case for relaxed selection is suggested in the higher frequencies of abnormal nasal septa among several Caucasian and one Far Eastern population as contrasted with a number of populations still living in food-collecting and primitive environments. This observation prompted a study published in 1966 of 2,353 skulls in twenty-two population samples, of which six are "civilized" and fourteen "primitive," the latter including aborigines of North America and Oceania.[4] The frequencies of septal deviations, spurs, ridges, or ledges of sufficient seriousness to suggest impairment of normal nose breathing were markedly higher in the former group of populations. This preliminary study can only be taken as suggestive; proof of relaxed selection for this trait requires further and more detailed studies, including studies of heritability and the effects of climate.

Other forms of selection may result from what would generally be considered improvements in our environment. A preliminary study of insufficient breast milk among recently delivered mothers indicates a genetic basis, with higher frequencies in populations having the longest history of domestic animal milk.[5] It seems likely that more cases of relaxed selection will be demonstrated as anthropological knowledge accumulates and adds to our understanding of human evolution during the past few millennia.

Relaxation of selection for certain physical characteristics was not the only change brought about by the new agricultural environment. One of the most noticeable differences between modern and primitive men is in the matter of immunity to contagious diseases. Among men today measles, scarlet fever, and a host of other communicable diseases are not a serious threat to life. Even before the advent of inoculations and antibiotics, they were considered children's diseases, and were seldom fatal. But among the groups of primitive peoples who were brought into contact with Europeans, such diseases wiped out whole populations. Geneticists seem quite well agreed that this greater immunity is due in large part to hereditary factors.[6a] The early hunters and food gatherers had lived in more or less isolated groups, and communicable diseases did not flourish or have a chance to become endemic. Immunity was not needed for survival, and there was little selection for immunity. But among the peoples living in farm communities, villages or towns, where such diseases could spread like wildfire, immunities had great survival value, and selection for these traits must have been going on for thousands of years among agricultural peoples. In this case selection was not relaxed, but intensified under the new conditions of the environment.

Among primitive men, early death must have taken an enormous toll; in some cases perhaps half of all children died before maturity. Even in the agricultural life of the past, it was not unusual for one-third of all children to die before reaching maturity. Today, among Western European peoples, less than 3% of all children die before their thirtieth year. In the industrialized modern state, many children who, because of some hereditary weakness, would not have survived a hundred years ago, are carried through to the age of reproduction by improved medical care and public health services; and many children who in the past would have died because their parents did not care for them properly, are carried through to adulthood by the welfare agencies of the state. This is more than relaxed selection, it represents a drastic diminishing in the rate of natural selection, tragic because it points to an increase in the proportion of people born to much suffering. Modern genetics with its growing understanding of the physical basis of heredity gives us many clues as to what is likely to develop out of such a situation.

◇◇◇◇◇

The Physical Basis of Heredity.

The mechanism of heredity provides that the nucleus of each fertilized ovum contains paired genetic factors or genes, one in each pair being from the father, and one being from the mother. Incredible as it may seem, there are probably tens of thousands of genes in each nucleus, though the nucleus it-self is too small to be seen in an ordinary microscope. The fertilized cell grows by duplication, and each pair of new nuclei are duplicates of the last. The cells provide the physi-cal structure, and the nucleus directs the development. Oc-casionally the mechanism for duplicating the nucleus goes astray. There is an aberration in the formation of one or more of the genes or an abnormality of the chromosomes in which the genes are located. Such a modification of the genes or chromosomes is called a "mutation." [7] It provides a novelty in the developmental instructions carried in each living human cell, an experimental novelty such as the chemist in his labora-tory might devise in his search for a new product. On rare oc-casions the experiment is a success and makes for an individual with an improved chance of survival. From such successful experiments have come all evolutionary advances.[8] But prob-ably 99% or more of the mutants produce some form of de-fect, such as hereditary disease, malformation, or weakness.[9] Some mutated genes called "dominants," have their effect when they are transmitted by only one parent. They cause the defect to show up in half of the children. Others, called "recessives," have their effect only when similar mutated genes are passed on by both parents. When both parents are car-riers of a similar recessive mutated gene, the inheritance will be, on the average, for every four children, one child without taint, two children carriers but not showing the defect, and one child defective. Some mutations are sex-linked; some

71

vary in completeness of effect, or "penetrance," some have a more complicated form of inheritance than that just described; and some may be effective only in conjunction with a combination of other genetic factors. This last case is called "polygenic" or "multifactoral" in contrast to single-gene inheritance. Single-gene inheritance is the easiest to trace, and much more is known about it than about polygenic inheritance.

Nature's process of experiment by mutation has been the source of evolutionary advance, but because so few of the experiments are successful it is also the cause of much human suffering. The suffering can never be eliminated altogether unless mutations can be stopped or their effect corrected, and in most cases this would require almost unimaginable advances in scientific knowledge and techniques. But the number of carriers and the offspring of carriers can be reduced, and the way this may be done is largely a matter of choice between various alternatives, some more and some less acceptable to the public.

Many defects spring entirely from heredity and seem quite unaffected by the environment in which development takes place. Such is the case in some forms of muscular dystrophy, for which there is no known cure and from which all affected children die before reaching maturity. At the other extreme is such a disease as lung cancer, in which inhaling cigarette smoke is a major cause, and breathing polluted air a lesser cause, both environmental; yet there appears to be some evidence for differences in hereditary susceptibility shown in studies in which a higher concentration of lung cancer appears in certain families.[10]

◇◇◇◇◇

The Frequency of Defects and Abnormalities.

Because of the interrelated effects of heredity and environment, geneticists are reluctant to give lists of "hereditary" diseases or defects. Recognizing that inclusion or noninclusion of a trait is to some extent arbitrary, Dobzhansky in his *Mankind Evolving* has noted 132 physical traits that are largely genetically determined.[11] Of these, 21 are metabolic disorders; 15 are defects of the skin; 28 are in the skeletal system; 7 in the teeth and mouth; 5 in the alimentary system; 14 blood and vascular; 2 urogenital; 19 relate to the eyes; 5 to disorders of the ear; and 16 to disorders of the nervous system and musculature. The list is, of course, incomplete and is confined to physical disorders, although some of the disorders of the nervous system result in mental degeneration or dementia. Many of the diseases in the list are known only by their Latin names and are quite rare, but some, like diabetes and myopia, are common, affecting millions of people. Even the less common defects take a terrible toll in human suffering. Some 200,-000 people in the United States have muscular dystrophy, most of them children in various progressive stages of the disease.[12] It is estimated that the serious physical defects taken together affect about 1% of all individuals at some time in their lives.[13]

Contagious or infectious diseases have high environmental components, though they are subject to genetic variation in susceptibility. Identical twins show a far greater concordance for tuberculosis and for paralytic poliomyelitis than do fraternal twins,[14] and to a less extent the same is true of measles and scarlet fever.[15] There seems little doubt that variations in susceptibility to many, perhaps most, contagious diseases are due to variations in genetic factors.[16]

Mental defects or deficiencies require separate consideration. One of the most common forms of mental illness, schizophrenia, is known to have both genetic and environmental causes. In a major study of twins in New York State,[17] Franz J. Kallmann found that the incidence of schizophrenia among relatives of schizophrenics increased with the closeness of the relationship; ranging from 7.1% for brothers or sisters, to 14% for fraternal co-twins, to 56.2% for identicals, and to 91.5% for identicals reared together. Other investigators have found concordances running from 9% for fraternal twins and 42% for identicals.[18] But concordance in identical twins is always short of 100%. It is clear that certain genotypes are subject in various degrees to schizophrenic breakdown, which some may escape with enough environmental good luck. Schizophrenics represent some 50% of the resident populations of mental hospitals.

About 3% to 5% of hospital residents are victims of manic-depressive psychosis.[19] The rest of the population of mental hospitals or institutions are mostly idiots, imbeciles, and feebleminded at a level at which they are not able to care for themselves, a group that the World Health Organization, in its report on Human Genetics and Public Health, lists as "low-grade mental defectives." [20] The report states that, "the low-grade defectives usually owe their condition to single accidents of development," although a certain proportion are affected by specific genetic conditions. The report says further, "With high-grade deficiency, essentially the lower end of the distribution of intelligence in the general population, the condition seems to be due to multiple causes, the genetic component being large and probably polygenic."

Schizophrenia affects about 1% of human populations, although in some areas the incidence is much higher.[21] Other mental defects and deficiencies may account for as much as one-half of 1% of most populations if we include those of sufficient intelligence to live outside of institutions but not of enough intelligence to be useful to society.

A third class of defects are the so-called constitutional or chronic and degenerative disorders, most of them determined by a single biochemical mechanism and by a variety of gene combinations.[22] It is difficult to estimate their frequency, because these conditions vary from extreme and disabling severity to no more than discomfort. They may affect 1% of all adults in fairly serious forms.

A summary of the injury caused by abnormal genetic factors would include serious physical defects and abnormalities affecting over 1% of all children born; something over 1% of the population suffering from incapacitating mental illnesses or feeblemindedness, and another considerable proportion, perhaps one half of 1%, or more, of adults affected by "constitutional," chronic and degenerative disorders.[23]

To this list of serious losses must be added the many genetically based minor defects that to a greater or less extent plague all of us in this imperfect world. We all have ills of one sort or another that, although they may have been brought on by environmental conditions, we would have escaped altogether if our genetic endowment had been without weaknesses. On the average we each carry an estimated four heterozygotes, i.e., single, lethal genes or lethal combinations of genes which if manifested in our offspring by a mating with a carrier of similar genes will cause death or failure to reproduce.[24] In addition we all carry many sublethal or subvital genes which may provide a basis for defect or illness in us or in our offspring. Geneticists estimate that a minimum of 10% of the sex cells and 20% of the progeny of humans in every generation carry newly arisen more or less harmful mutants.[25] This seems like a large number of new mutations, but it falls into perspective when we realize that each human cell has at least ten thousand genes, perhaps many more, and the mutation of a tiny fraction of these numerous genes adds up to a considerable number in each individual. Geneticists have studied the frequency of mutation for various types of deleterious genes. Their estimates range from .1 per hundred thousand for the gene that results in Huntington's Chorea, to .8 per hundred thousand for muscular dystrophy, 2 or 3 per hundred thousand for hemophilia, and as high as 10 per hundred thousand for the gene for a certain type of tumor of the nervous tissue [26] which shows up in about 1 out of every

3,000 births. Estimates of the mutation rate have been made for only a few of the injurious genes that are more easily followed in the family line. Estimates are not yet available for the great majority of less harmful mutants, which are hard to trace, because they may do little if any injury.[27]

Dominant mutant genes that always cause death or failure to reproduce die off with the death of the carrier. None goes on to the next generation. Their frequency in the population is no greater than the frequency of the new mutations. But most mutant genes do not cause the death of the carrier. Dominants, even near lethal ones, may have various degrees of penetrance or may have their effect modified by a particular environment, or may produce an abnormality which makes marriages or reproduction less likely, thus slowly reducing the frequency of the gene.

Recessive mutants continue in the population until they are paired with another of the same kind and together produce the defect that diminishes their chance of survival. Thus the genetic load of each generation consists of new mutations plus the mutated genes carried over from the past, only a fraction dying off in each generation. The recessive mutant genes are carried over in much the highest proportion, because they usually have no serious effects until they are paired. The likelihood of such a pairing of mutant genes increases with their frequency in the population. Eventually each mutant gene reaches a point of equilibrium at which the number of mutated genes dying out equals the number of new mutations. Stern makes an estimate (which he considers little more than an educated guess) that there are about fifty times as many detrimental mutant genes in each generation of the population as would be produced by new mutations.[28] The proportion of course differs for each different type of mutant. Achondroplastic dwarfs whose defect is due to a dominant gene, and who are selected against chiefly because they have so few children, are present in the population both because of new mutations, arising at the estimated rate of four per 100,000 sex cells and also because of mutations carried over from previous generations. In the case of these dwarfs, the accumulation of detrimental dominant mutants has risen until it about equals the number of new mutants produced in each generation, at which point an equilibrium appears to have been reached, mutants dying out as rapidly as new mutants are being formed.[29]

In the case of recessive gene mutations the situation is quite different, because the defect they are responsible for will occur only when there is a mating of two people, each of whom carries a similar mutated gene, and then only with a probability of affecting one in four of their children. If mating is at random, the chances of such a mating are in proportion to the frequency of the gene in the population, and it may take a long time, and a great increase in the number of such genes, before a point of equilibrium is reached, and the number of the genes dying out equals the number of new mutations. The relatively mild recessive defect of albinism arises by mutation with a frequency of perhaps 2.8 per 100,000. But it is not heavily selected against and the frequency has increased until perhaps 1% of the sex cells in the population carry albinism. At 1% frequency and with random mating, the mating of two carriers would occur once in 10,000 marriages,[30] and the actual defect, since the gene is recessive, would be found in one out of four of the children of such marriages. In the case of amaurotic idiocy, a recessive gene that is lethal when paired, the frequency of the gene in the population will be three hundred times greater than the mutation frequency.[31]

On the whole, for all harmful mutated genes, the number of carriers is far greater than the number of people showing the defect. We may carry only a few lethal genes or lethal combinations of genes out of our complement of ten thousand or more, and the chance of a mating with someone carrying an identical mutation is small. But in the case of nonlethal, less serious mutations, of which we carry a greater number, the chances of a mating between carriers is proportionately greater; it is estimated that over 2% of all children born carry some fairly serious hereditary defect as a result of such matings.[32] This is for the population as a whole. If we consider only consanguineous marriages, the rate of defect is substantially higher because related family stocks are likely to carry the same type of mutated gene.

◇◇◇◇◇

Genetic Equilibrium and the Genetic Load.

Some one hundred or more years ago, before we moved fully into the modern environment of public health, therapy, and radiation, the balance of mutated deleterious genes was prob-

79

ably about at equilibrium, the loss of genes for defect in each generation balancing the accretion from new mutations. Since then, a number of things have been happening to change the balance. Young people move around more than they used to. They have a wider choice of mates and do not marry so often within neighboring or related family stocks. There is less chance of their marrying someone with similar mutated genes, and this makes for a reduction in the number of defects in the next generation. But for that very reason it increases the frequency of recessive mutated genes in the population as a whole, since with fewer matings between carriers and fewer defective persons, selection does not have a chance to eliminate so many of the genes. Eventually, as carriers become more and more frequent and matings between carriers increase, the proportion of defect will rise and more of the deleterious genes will die off. A new equilibrium will be established with more of the genes in the population and a higher rate of defect. At one percent frequency in the population, marriage between carriers would be one in 10,000; at two percent frequency, marriage between carriers would be one in 2,500, which is four times more frequent. The rule against cousin marriages is a good rule for the individuals concerned because it reduces the possibility of having a defective child. But it is harmful to society because it only postpones the day when the defect will appear, and then in greater numbers than before because the gene has increased in frequency.

Another change that affects the genetic equilibrium is the increase in man-made radiation. This may be from the use of X rays in medical diagnosis, from radiation released from the atomic energies released by bombs or atomic plants, or from chemicals and other sources. Geneticists estimate that man-made radiation alone in the United States has about doubled the exposure of man's hereditary materials to radiation.[33] Radiation is not the only cause of mutations, and scientists cannot but be concerned with the possible spread of defects and abnormalities in our rapidly changing environment.

An even more serious threat to the genetic equilibrium is the saving of life through new medical techniques and improved public-health measures. There is cause for rejoicing that death rates, which only a short time ago were forty or more per thousand of population per year, are now down to eight or ten. But there are penalties attaching to this advance. Selection is greatly relaxed for all the vast numbers of people who have been saved from death and enabled to reproduce their kind with the help of modern medicine and under the protection of new measures of public health. The deleterious genes that are thus saved from immediate destruction will be added to those already in circulation, until a new equilibrium is reached, and defects begin appearing at a greater rate than before.

There will be a delay in the appearance of an increased number of defects because the increase in the number and frequency of carriers for mutated genes must precede an increase in the number of matings. But about the time the new equilibrium is getting established, the increase in defect will be sudden and frightening in extent. These changes are cumulative, but they take place slowly. It will take many generations, in some cases perhaps a thousand years, before the genetic load reaches these new and dangerous equilibriums.

Some geneticists and biologists look upon this situation with the gravest concern. C. P. Richter believes that in the technologically advanced countries natural selection has come to a halt—the unfit survive and reproduce their kind and "Man's biological twilight is approaching." [34] Nobel Prize winner, H. J. Muller, is equally pessimistic. He sees the time coming when "our descendants' natural biological organization would in fact have disintegrated and have been replaced by complete disorder. . . . It would in the end be far easier and more sensible to manufacture a complete new man *de novo*, out of appropriately chosen raw materials, than to try to refashion into human form those pitiful relics which remained." [35]

But eminent geneticists including Dobzhansky, Wallace, and many others, do not think that our present limited knowledge justifies such a dire assessment of man's probable future. The science of genetics is still in its infancy and present evaluations of the biological meaning and social import of genetic loads are necessarily tentative. [36] But even the most optimistic geneticists agree that the probable increase of genetic defects and deficiencies poses a serious threat to man's future.

5

Eugenic Policies and Proposals

◇◇

The Chronology of Eugenic Proposals.

Francis Galton, a cousin of Charles Darwin, made the first objective studies in the field of eugenics. He devised new statistical methods which are an important tool of social science research. Through his extensive studies of twins he gave the first scientific proof of the part played by heredity in individual differences. But his studies did not go far enough. He failed to recognize the environmental disadvantages of the British lower classes, and attributed their low intelligence to poor heredity.

There was in Galton's time no science of genetics. Mendel's work had not been recognized, and the various theories of heredity then current gave no indication of the great complexity of human inheritance or the method of its transmission. Most important of all, there was at that time no appreciation of the part that was soon to be played by contraception. Hardly anyone foresaw that some day soon man would interfere with the natural processes of conception and birth.

Galton was a man of genius, and also eminently sensible and practical. The eugenic measures that he proposed were appropriate to the knowledge then available. He urged young men of superior family stocks not to marry heiresses, since an heiress was usually an only child, likely in turn to have few children herself. He proposed fellowships for able students, so that they might marry and produce a family. He gave consideration to special inducements to superior young people to raise large families. He devised various forms for keeping family records, and urged their general use. Above all he urged further study and education along eugenic lines. He believed that the improvement of the race should be man's highest aspiration, toward which all men should work.[1]

A wave of unscientific eugenic proposals were triggered in the United States around the turn of the century by the studies on the Juke[2] and Kallikak[3] families, and by the difficulty of assimilating the great wave of immigrations, which reached a peak of one million immigrants yearly in 1910. The

Juke study traced a degenerate family line through five generations of degenerates, thieves, prostitutes, and ne'er-do-wells—all descended from a common ancestor known as "Old Horror," the product of a mating between a worthy colonial and a prostitute; while the same colonial, marrying into a good family, begat a notable line of high-grade descendants. The Kallikak story was of a similar kind. Both studies showed that the generations tend to follow the pattern set by the parents, but neither study distinguished the effects of a bad environment. Heredity alone was held to blame, and the evidence seemed to show the need for laws to restrict the breeding of "degenerate" stocks.

When it was indicated that immigrants from southern Europe included a high proportion of feebleminded and otherwise defective people, it was easy to argue that failure to assimilate was due to hereditary weaknesses rather than to the handicaps the immigrants faced in the New World. Legislative hearings on a new immigration law were replete with eugenic arguments, which undoubtedly affected the outcome —the Quota System, which was not revised until 1965. During the same period eugenic sterilization laws were passed in some twenty-one states, providing for the voluntary or compulsory sterilization of the feebleminded and in some cases of criminals. In both the national legislation resulting in the quota act, and the state legislation on sterilization, the eugenic argument had been overworked. The evidence for heredity was based on inadequate studies, and racial prejudices corrupted the nature of the evidence. The National Origins Act was kept on the books, not because the appeal to heredity was justified, but because immigrants had been coming in at a rate too rapid for the country to absorb. The eugenic sterilization laws were rarely invoked, and except in California and Indiana they became practically a dead letter. Public opinion was not aroused to demand their enforcement, and continuing studies showed that environment as well as heredity must be recognized as a frequent cause of mental deficiency. Eugenic proposals had been enacted into law without the scientific evidence to support them. Racial and emotional prejudices had played a part. When later Hitler prostituted eugenics, the American public was ready to drop the word from its vocabulary.

The English eugenists had been more cautious in their appraisal of the knowledge then available. Their proposals remained pretty much in line with Galton's, but with greater emphasis on the "better" family. There was no means of separating heredity from environment in the criteria for determining the "better" families. Too large a proportion came from the upper classes to which the eugenists themselves belonged. It was hard to interest the mass of the people in proposals for increasing births among the upper classes. The eugenist had not learned the lesson that when eugenics becomes self-conscious it tends to lose its virtue.

In the United States, radical proposals for eugenic insemination were put forward as early as 1940 by the late Dr. H. J. Muller.[4] Dr. Muller was an eminent geneticist who won the Nobel Prize for his work on the effect of X rays on mutations. It is said that each year in the United States over ten thousand women who are not able to have children by their husbands are being inseminated with the sperm of donors.[5] The names of the donors are carefully concealed and it appears that in most cases there is little or no investigation of their probable genetic quality. Dr. Muller proposed that the use of insemination should be increased. He recommended the establishment of sperm banks which would make available the sperm of highly qualified donors whose family histories showed the least possible likelihood of defect or abnormality. In order to make sure of the eminence of the donors and to give time for a test of their progeny, the sperm would be frozen and made widely available only after twenty years or more, when the donor would no longer be alive, and posterity could judge dispassionately of his value. This would also avoid the complications which arise today when women who have been impregnated desire, as they sometimes do, to meet the successful donor.

It is a shocking commentary on public ignorance of genetics that so little concern is shown for the quality of the donor in inseminations. Muller's proposals deserve serious backing if they are for the present limited to the use now being made of insemination. They would not only safeguard the women being inseminated, but over the years they would provide answers to questions that are impossible to answer without a considerable period of trial.

A number of questions should be answered before extending insemination to any great proportion of the population. Some of the questions are purely genetic. In the present state of knowledge even the best of geneticists might disagree as to who should be donors without a prolonged study of the type of inheritance desired and the accompanying mechanism of heredity. It is not likely that women desiring to be inseminated, and given a voluntary choice as to the donor, would make the same choice as the geneticist, or a wiser one. Geneticists would want an extended trial, including a progeny test, to make sure that the donor's descendants were free of genetic defect and likely to be endowed with high qualities of intelligence and character.

Insemination also raises many social and practical questions which need to be answered before it is generally adopted. What kind of woman in general would ask to be inseminated? What would be the effect on the marriage relation, on the attitudes of the husband toward a child so adopted, on the child itself? However important we may consider heredity in the making of a valuable citizen, we cannot disregard the effect on the child of the attitudes of the parents and the environmental conditions of the home. Deep and instinctive emotional reactions are involved in such a change from all the past experience of the race. It would be dangerous to violate them without more knowledge of what might happen. Experience in this field has been limited to women who have been inseminated because they were unable to have children by their husbands, and observation of even this selected sample has raised a number of questions. We do not

88

know how many women would, in actual practice, desire a child by someone other than their husbands, or what kind of society would evolve if the majority of men were deprived of the happiness and responsibility of fathering their own sons.

Muller proposed, in effect, that we would breed from selected donors, chosen originally by qualified judges, and selected from this group by women desiring children. It is essentially a plan for arbitrary breeding based on the application of present knowledge in this complex field. As Muller himself has pointed out, there is danger that it might be misused.

The radical nature of Muller's proposals are in sharp contrast to the more conservative and socially acceptable proposals now generally approved by social scientists and geneticists who have engaged in work in this field. These proposals fall under two headings: those for the reduction of defects, and those for the improvement of intelligence, and both will be discussed in this order.

◇◇◇◇◇

Proposals for the Reduction of Defects.

In the not too distant past most people thought of a hereditary "taint" as an act of God, something beyond man's control, even perhaps as a punishment for past sins. God visited the sins of the father upon his children even to the third and fourth generation. Today we know that mutations and their haphazard results are part of the law under which God moves to creation and evolutionary advance. But individuals and families still find it hard to shed the sense of guilt and achieve enough maturity to face problems of hereditary defect in a responsible way. Too many people make every effort to hide the taint that is in their family, and even to hide the truth from themselves, and this can have tragic consequences for them and for their children. The attitude toward Huntington's Chorea furnishes an extreme but terrible example of this. The disease comes on in middle age, usually after the children are born, and starts with a breakdown of the central nervous system, running into a fatal and sometimes dangerous dementia.[6] There is no cure, nor anything known to slow its course. It is a dominant trait; on the average, half of the children of the afflicted person will inherit it. The families who carry this gene try, quite generally, to keep it a secret, even from the children of the family, often to the extent of moving to another locality where they are not known. Then the children may in turn be married and after a while face the terrible knowledge that they have brought this tragedy on their children.

A change in attitudes is an essential step toward the development of policies for reducing defects and abnormalities that have a genetic origin.

Fortunately the climate for such a change is rapidly improving with the advance of knowledge in the field of what is now called "medical genetics." Immediately after World War II the medical schools in the United States greatly increased their interest in heredity and began research and teaching in the genetics of defects, abnormalities, and susceptibility to disease. By 1964 the World Health Organization in its Report on Human Genetics and Public Health, stated that "problems of defect and abnormality are considered the responsibility of medical and public health services." [7] Advances have been made in the detection of carriers and in methods of treatment. Most important from the point of view of eugenics, some twenty-six or more medical schools in the United States are now operating heredity clinics, where couples can go for information about the probability, or risk, of their having a defective child.

Heredity clinics are the first eugenic proposals that have been adopted in a practical form and accepted by the public. They are run by scientists and their findings are based on scientific knowledge. The word eugenics is not associated with them. The couples who go to them for advice are interested in not having an abnormal child, rather than in the less personal goal of improving the race. If they suspect that they may be carriers of a particular deleterious gene or group of genes, they want to know whether their children will suffer the defect. It is the function of the heredity clinic, after careful examination of the family record, to advise on the chances of the defect being passed on to the children. Reports from these clinics indicate that couples are considerably influenced by the information they receive in the clinics, and generally, but not always, they are influenced in a eugenic direction.

Heredity clinics will become more important with every advance in knowledge of human genetics and with every increase in the education of the public.[8]

Institutional care has important eugenic implications. It has been provided for helpless persons in this country since colonial days. It was certainly not introduced for eugenic reasons, but it has been an important factor in preventing seriously defective persons from having children. Institutional care should be considerably extended for both social and eugenic reasons.

In several states laws have been passed to provide for sterilization before release from institutional care. A California law of this sort was approved by the Supreme Court with Justice Oliver Wendell Holmes' famous dictum, "Three generations of imbeciles are enough."[9] But heredity is not the only cause of feeblemindedness, and there is a strong public feeling against compulsory sterilization. Voluntary sterilization, which is frequently used for eugenic reasons, is being extended and may come to have important eugenic value.

Now that there are available methods of contraception, such as the IUD, that are effective over long periods without the need for restraint or care, there should be little objection to preventing pregnancies to women who do not want a child and are not qualified to care for one.

Efforts should be made to reduce births among individuals in this country who suffer from mental defect or deficiency at a level just above that which would require their hospitalization. Their marriage rate is fortunately low, but those who do marry or live with a common-law mate have more children than the average of the rest of the population, although they are not competent to bring them up. Recent studies made in England indicate that couples at a low level of intelligence, either from biological or environmental causes, do not want many pregnancies and will take advantage of contraception if given a chance.[10] No attempt was made in these English studies to distinguish those whose deficiencies were of a hereditary sort; the women were grouped according to their condition, not its cause. The studies clearly show that it is possible, with the proper approach, to get a voluntary reduction of births among women at the lower levels of mental competence. A reduction of births at this level would be an important contribution to reducing the frequency of genes which make for mental defect. There would also be an immediate gain to society because fewer children would be born to suffer from an inadequate environment.

Finally, at a level somewhat above that of the mentally deficient, there are a substantial number of families among whom employment is irregular, who are constantly on and off relief, and who are generally well known to all the social and welfare agencies of their community. Where such families have congregated in isolated groups, they may show a high proportion of serious genetic defects.[11] In general, among such families, the environment in which their children are brought up provides too little stimulus for normal development. Their

birth rate is high, and their large families make it more difficult for them to break out of the dreary cycle of poverty, little
education, and large families. Yet recent studies indicate that
probably as many as half their children result from pregnancies that are not wanted at the time, or ever, by one or both
parents.[12] Such couples should not be denied the opportunity
to use the new methods of contraception that are available to
better-off families. A reduction in the number of their unwanted children would further both the social and the biological improvement of the population; the social improvement because children resulting from unwanted pregnancies
do not have as good a chance as wanted children; and the
biological improvement because a reduction in births among
any of such groups having even a slightly above-average proportion of defect or deficiency would make for a reduction in
genetic defects.[13]

Thus there are four presently available means of reducing
the incidence of deleterious genes, each socially acceptable
and each wholly voluntary: (1) the heredity clinic; (2) the
better application of institutional care; (3) training and constant help in the use of the new methods of contraception for
the mentally defective and borderline cases not in institutions;
and (4) making available the new forms of contraception to
the great number of people at the lower economic and educational levels where the older methods have been ineffective
even when available. All these things are being done to some
extent at the present time. If they had behind them the force
of a strong public opinion, they could have a considerably

increased effect in slowing down the increase in hereditary defect that seems to be moving in on us.

The most important research now going on is that on the detection of carriers. Medical geneticists already know how to detect the carriers of some fifteen or twenty serious defects, and methods for identifying carriers of other defects are being developed. For every carrier of a recessive gene who can be detected, additional people will consult heredity clinics, and the advice given by the clinics will have a sounder base.

Eugenists have long urged the keeping of family records to provide information on family traits, particularly those related to defects or deficiencies. Such records are of great interest to medical genetics and would help to provide warnings against the marriage or childbearing of carriers of deleterious recessive strains. However, the public has shown little interest in questions that most people would rather avoid. In a few states the public health authorities have made extensive studies of particular diseases and have made careful records of carrier families. But unless this is done on a nationwide basis, it is difficult to trace the spread of the suspected genes, and so far the federal government has shown little interest. In the Scandinavian countries, government institutions have kept extensive records of this sort, and so are in a far better position to work out measures for reducing genetic abnormalities, by segregation in institutions, by sterilization, or by the use of modern means of contraception. It is unlikely that the American government will do anything along these lines except under the pressure of public opinion. That will only be aroused when the public comes to realize the extent of the genetic contribution to the toll of human suffering in this country, and how fast it is increasing.

Finally there is the possibility, remote and impossible as it may seem today, that science will develop the knowledge and the techniques for changing specific genes in desired ways. But even this *deus ex machina* might come too late if the deterioration of the race had passed the point of no return.

The immediate problem is the relief of human suffering. In countries where few children die before reaching maturity and the average span of life is over seventy years, the greatest cause of physical suffering is the inheritance of some defect or deficiency. Over 1% of all populations suffer from some fairly severe form of mental illness during their lifetimes. Two percent of all children of school age in the United States are sufficiently retarded in their intellectual development to need either institutional care or special educational provision to attain their fullest possible development, and much of this retardation has a genetic base. Add to these the load of physical defects, including hereditary deafness, blindness, the muscular dystrophies, diabetes, and many others, and we must conclude that not less than 4% of all our people are burdened at some time in their own lives and are a burden to their families because of some chronic and incurable weakness. What proportion of this load of suffering is due to hereditary factors is hard to estimate. Each case is a special one. But on the average we can be fairly sure that at least half are due to the influence of a poor heredity, perhaps considerably more than half. Two percent is then a conservative figure, and two percent of 200 million people is 4,000,000 persons who are suffering themselves and bringing tragedy to their families.

It will never be possible to do away with all genetic defects. A certain proportion is due to newly arisen mutations that cannot be prevented; another proportion is due to the continued life of mutated genes which confer an advantage when inherited in the heterozygous state, an advantage that may offset the injury done to the homozygotes who will carry the defect. The frequency of dominant genes which produce defect might be greatly reduced by wholly acceptable measures in a couple of generations and ultimately almost eliminated. Recessive genes for defect could be reduced considerably during the first one or two generations of those subjected to a system of control, but reduction to a point near the rate of new mutations would be a matter of many generations.

Alternative means for reducing the incidence of defect will be proposed from time to time by scientists, and the public will have to decide which means are acceptable. They will probably decide on the more moderate proposals. There are many considerations to be taken into account other than the strictly genetic. Perhaps the most important function of the public is to create a climate of opinion that will put pressure on carriers of defect to reduce their reproduction, and on scientists in medicine and public health to put priority on all studies that might provide leads for effective action.

A better understanding of heredity, frank recognition of the personal and social problems arising at every level, open discussion, and a sense of each individual's obligation to his children and to the community of man—all these are essential to success in reducing the heavy load of hereditary defect.

❖❖❖❖❖

Proposals for Raising the Level of Intelligence.

We have seen in Chapter 2 that since 1930 birth differentials between groups at different educational levels have narrowed, and in the near future may even favor the better educated. Along with the narrowing of birth differentials between groups, there is new evidence that the more successful or high IQ individuals within each group may soon be having more children than the less intelligent individuals in the group. The material in Chapter 3 indicates that these trends are favorable to genetic improvement. If they can be continued they should, along with the advantages of having a larger proportion of children born and brought up in better than average home surroundings, raise the average level of intelligence to a very substantial degree.

The spread of birth control may not be the cause of these trends, but it certainly has made them possible. The most urgent eugenic policy at this time is to see that birth control is made equally available to all individuals in every class of society. This is a practical objective, generally approved of by public opinion today. It will be made easier by the improved and cheaper methods of birth control now being developed.

There are today in the United States large numbers of people who, through lack of birth control information or services and lack of initiative, either do not use contraception or do not use it effectively. Most of these persons do not want the number of children they are now having. Until these individuals learn to regulate the number of their children to those they really want and are willing to be responsible for, no system of voluntary eugenics will be fully effective. Making contraception available to them will be difficult, but it is certainly not an impossible task, and is a most urgent step in implementing eugenic policy.

Full availability of contraception does not guarantee that the present trend toward genetic improvement will continue. The distribution of births as well as their number may be changed by new circumstances. There are fewer births in a depression, more births in good times; but we do not know how different types of people are affected by such changes in conditions.

Perhaps the most important eugenic development, second only to the extension of birth control, is the scientific study of factors which affect decisions as to size of family among different types of parents under different circumstances. The problems involved are capable of scientific solutions and are appropriate only to scientists trained in these fields of study. The nonprofessional who puts forward ideas in these areas is likely to find that they lack scientific confirmation and confuse rather than help the eugenic cause.

This has certainly been the case in the past, and we must hope that it will not happen too often in the future.

It may take some time to develop effective eugenic policies based on competent scientific studies of the factors which affect size of family. But meantime there is much that can be done along the lines indicated by our present knowledge and experience. We know, for instance, that in many large groups in the United States people tend to a rather uniform size of family. In the period after World War II it has been the fashion among high school and college graduates to have three or four children. During the great Depression of the thirties the fashion for high school and college people was for one or two children. In both periods those who went outside the number of children usual at the time were often made to feel that their behavior was odd, perhaps even antisocial. Such a standardization of size of family at whatever level is not compatible with a eugenic form of society. In order to provide a distribution of births favorable to eugenic improvement, there must be considerable variations in size of family within every group. This requires a public opinion with sufficient discrimination to appreciate larger families among responsible parents and to be impatient of irresponsible parents who bring children into a world in which they will get little care. It is not a matter of giving advice. It is rather a matter of the attitudes of those who help form public opinion in matters affecting the family. Doctors, ministers, and priests are close to the family, and their attitudes will have an important bearing on the many people they come in contact with.[14] For people on relief or otherwise in contact with social agencies, a discriminating attitude on the part of community social workers together with advice on the availability of birth control should have a substantial effect. At every level of society there are responsible couples who desire children and should be encouraged and helped to have the children they can care for. Other couples who are irresponsible in regard to childbearing, whether wealthy divorcées or persons on relief, should feel the weight of an adverse public opinion, instead of the favorable attitudes which now too often accompany their childbearing. Community leaders of every kind should encourage this kind of wise discrimination.

Eugenics is much concerned with the selection of mates. Assortative mating, the mating of like with like, brings together constellations of genes alike for specialized qualities and concentrates them in family lines. Then if such traits as intelligence or musical ability or physical endurance are favored for survival, they survive in concentrated form, and mate selection becomes an important agent of selection. Genetic improvement therefore favors marriages based on similarity of qualities rather than on social class or geographical proximity. In the early days in this country the opportunity for finding a mate was limited to the relatively few people who were within walking or riding distance of the home. Today by plane and auto, in high school and college, young people meet each other in great numbers and variety; but there is need for a better acquaintance and more thoughtful judgment in the choice of one's mate. Education to this end should be a part of any sound eugenic program.

As more is learned about the conditions that determine size of family among different kinds of people, new ways will be found to modify our social institutions for the specific purpose of increasing the proportion of children born to those who achieve most within the limits of their particular environment, and at the same time decreasing the proportion of children born to those with least achievement in their environment. Changes of this sort will be the more easily accepted because they are also favorable to social advance, in that they increase the proportion of children brought up in the more responsible homes in every environment.

The consideration of policies for providing a social environment which will encourage eugenic trends leads to a concept new to eugenic thinking. Since the goal of eugenics is to further conditions in which the generality of men will be increasingly competent in their particular environments, we must be concerned that these environments will reflect man's higher aspirations. An environment in which the rewards go to the unscrupulous, the incompetent, or the lazy, might encourage an increase in human stocks with just such characteristics. A voluntary system of eugenics such as may be developed out of present trends would be satisfactory only if the environment for which men were being selected was of a sort which satisfied the ideals of thoughtful men. The effort to improve the environment has always been a matter of concern. It will become increasingly important as men realize that the interests of hereditary improvement are also served in this indirect way. The improvement of the environment is as important as the improvement of the hereditary base, for the two are closely related in the evolutionary process.

Many present trends are helping to lay a base for the development of a eugenic form of society. There are trends toward the equalization of educational opportunity, so that hereditary ability wherever found will have a better chance to show itself. There is an increase in social and occupational mobility, so that each individual will more easily find the work for which his particular heredity most fits him. Finally, there is the trend discussed above, the one toward more well-considered mate selection and assortative mating, which will make for the improvement of special types and make possible an increase in selection. These trends provide the framework for eugenic policies which would increase the diversity of human stocks at a constantly higher level of ability, selected only by the pressures of an environment favoring the survival of those whose achievement exceeds that of their immediate neighbors. Such policies envisage a form of unselfconscious selection not unlike the natural selection that took place throughout the long period of man's evolution.

Eugenic policies for improving the hereditary base of intelligence and character must thus take into account the conditions under which men live and work and lead their daily lives, insofar as these conditions affect the survival of different family lines. The aim of eugenic proposals is an increase in the proportion of children born to the individuals who are most successful in their particular environment, and a decrease in the proportion of children born to the least successful in their environment. Eugenics seeks conditions under which no able stocks would be neglected, wherever they may be found, and in which every social, occupational, and educational group would in each succeeding generation have a larger proportion of children with a better than average capacity for success in their particular environment.

Measures for improving the hereditary base of intelligence and character can be made effective on a voluntary basis without arousing in the individual any conscious concern for eugenic results. It is well that this is so. Eugenic goals are most likely to be attained under a name other than eugenics. It is not a good thing for individuals to classify themselves or others by gradations of hereditary superiority. Out of a long experience, the public has an instinctive distrust of any assumption of superiority by any individual, class or race. Such assumptions have long been used to maintain the status quo, and to prevent ability from rising in a static society.

The policies now generally accepted by students of eugenics in the United States are different from those that were proposed in the nineteen-thirties and are still associated in the public mind with the word eugenics. The old proposals had no solid scientific base; the newer eugenic policies are based on recent large-scale studies of population trends in this country and on the recent findings of geneticists, sociologists, and psychologists. Many of the old proposals sprang from emotional bias, with racial or class overtones; they did violence to American ideals and were contrary to existing habits and attitudes. The new eugenic policies do not give offense to the habits and customs established in the long experience of mankind; they are compatible with the highest American ideals; they propose to reinforce trends that are already under way and to reinforce them in ways which the public is wholly willing to accept. Everyone wants children to be wanted children, born to parents who will give them homes where they will have the best and most affectionate care and a fine parental example. Achievement in building a home as well as success in other aspects of life constitutes a eugenic criterion today just as it did during the long period of man's evolution when achievement meant survival. Proposals based on such criteria are the best we can be sure of at present. They are fully acceptable to the public. Every advance of science will modify and enlarge them.

These are not dramatic proposals. It would be hard to make a rallying cry for a great eugenic movement out of ideas most of which have long been accepted for purely environmental reasons. Yet these simple and generally unobjectionable proposals, now directed to a eugenic purpose, would, if properly carried out, not only increase the proportion of children brought up in a better-than-average home environment, but would at the same time raise the average hereditary potential of each succeeding generation. Every occupational group, every social group, and every educational group would be affected and improved, and a greater variety of improved abilities would be made available for the innumerable various tasks of our complex civilization.

The measures envisaged by the eugenist for raising the genetic level are also measures envisaged by the environmentalist for raising the level of the environment in which children are reared. It makes no difference which is the more important, both are taken into account. Each improvement in genetic capacity enables the individual to take better advantage of the improved environment, and the average of developed and measurable intelligence and character is raised accordingly in each generation. Change in the average is accompanied by an even greater change at the extremes. There would be a much increased proportion of people at the highest levels of intelligence and character, and a much diminished proportion of people at the lowest levels of intelligence and character. No other improvement in human society could so greatly affect the future of man.

6

The Future of Human Heredity

◇◇◇

Is the human race deteriorating? Is an advanced civilization incompatible with those processes of selection that are necessary for holding down the level of defect and maintaining or raising the levels of intelligence and character in succeeding generations? These questions could perhaps be answered if we knew the changes that lie ahead in human societies. Lacking such prophetic powers, we can only assess the trends that we see developing in this and other countries and each draw our own conclusions for their future significance.

Of the major trends affecting the hereditary qualities

of future generations, two seem quite certain to continue until they have spread throughout all the world's people. These are the increasing use and effectiveness of contraception, and the reduction of early deaths through advances in medicine and public health.

The spread of contraception is perhaps the most important of these trends. It is an inevitable corollary of the reduction in early deaths and the lengthening span of life. We cannot for long have one without the other. If deaths are reduced without reducing births, the population outgrows its resources. If births are reduced without a corresponding reduction in deaths, the population moves toward extinction. The recognition recently given this relationship by people and governments, together with the almost universal desire of people all over the world not to have more children than they can support, seems to indicate that the trend toward increasing use of contraception will continue. At the same time the improved methods of contraception now being developed make for a more effective and more rational control of births.

The trend toward the control of early deaths also seems likely to continue all over the world. In the past 150 years the expectation of life at birth of the American people has increased from less than 45 years to over 70. In Western Europe the increase is even greater. In the less industrialized countries, where the expectation of life is still in many cases less than 45 years, the reduction in deaths is taking place more rapidly than it did in Europe or the United States. As an example of the speed with which deaths can be reduced by simple modern methods, the death rates in Ceylon went down from 19.8 per thousand in 1946 to 9.8 per thousand in 1956. The greater part of the reduction came from the reduction of malaria and other insect-born diseases and the introduction of pure drinking water, all at a low cost per capita. In most of Asia, Africa, and South America the death rate is going down more rapidly than the birth rate, thereby threatening dangerous pressures of population upon developed resources. But in the long view of genetic change this is a temporary matter, important only as far as it may affect the future form of society.

These two trends, the reduction of early deaths through medicine and public health, and the reduction of births through voluntary contraception, have greatly changed the processes of genetic selection. Differences in deaths play a smaller part than in the past; differences in births between different kinds of people play a larger part. Deaths were a matter over which the individual and even society itself, had little control. Births are today fast becoming a matter almost wholly within the control of the individual, who is guided by his personal interests and influenced by the form of the society he lives in.

The result of cutting down on the death rate can be forecast into the foreseeable future with some assurance. There will be an increase throughout the population in the frequency of mutated genes responsible for serious hereditary defects and abnormalities, and this will be followed in due time by an increase in actual defects. The basis for such a forecast can be simply stated. Medicine and public health are saving the lives of many people in their early years and making possible their reproduction. Of this number there are many who only a short time ago would not have lived to pass on their defective genes to the next generation. At the same time the increase in radiation and in chemical and other "mutagenic" agents in the industrialized countries will almost certainly make for a higher rate of deleterious mutations. This increase in mutations, accompanied by a lower rate of elimination by death, would, unless other factors intervene, inevitably increase the frequency of the deleterious genes. We may expect then, for a long time to come, an increase in the already heavy burden of serious hereditary defects and abnormalties, alleviated only by the efforts of doctors to improve and lengthen the lives of the victims. Geneticists differ on the ultimate danger involved. As previously noted in Chapter 4, Section d, some hold that "man's biological twilight is approaching." Others believe that before we reach a critical point we will have greatly increased our knowledge of carriers and will have taken steps to minimize their reproduction. The "deterioration of the race" may be a future danger. As yet, however, it can hardly be said to have set in.

Other than serious defects and abnormalities, there will undoubtedly be an increase in the proportion of those small changes, hardly to be called defects, which offer no hazard to survival in our comfortable civilized life, but which would have diminished the chance of survival in more primitive times. An example is eye defects, which can easily be corrected by glasses. Such minor changes are the result of "relaxed selection." To people living with the amenities of civilization they present no danger to life or to prospects of marrying and having children. But they certainly represent a departure from that greater physical and mental perfection that should be the birthright of every human being.

The changes resulting from the spread of contraception are difficult to assess. In the industrialized countries, birth rates seem to be stabilizing at a point where families of two or three children are the norm in each of the different socio-economic classes. This is close to the number actually desired by most parents, as indicated by many carefully controlled studies. Even in the countries presently less industrialized, recent studies indicate that the people want no more than two or three or four children as long as the death rate is low enough to assure their survival. At present they are having far more than this number. In some areas, as noted in Chapter 2, the average is as high as eight children per married woman. But births are quite definitely going down, and with the increasing use of contraception it seems likely that within a few generations, families averaging two or three children will be the norm over most of the world. At these low birth rates, even a small proportion of no-child and one-child families, and a fair proportion of five-or-six-child families, can provide the base for large changes in hereditary qualities from one generation to another (see pp. 54–56). The hereditary future of the race will be largely determined by the amounts of such variations below and above the average, and by the types of people involved. If there is a substantial proportion of no-child and one-child families, and if the family lines in this group have more than the average number of genes for defect, their failure to reproduce will offset, to a greater or less degree, the increase in genes for defect expected because of a reduced death rate. If at the same time there is substantial proportion of families of four, five and six or more, and if these families are above the average in hereditary capacity for intelligence, their above-average birth rate will increase the proportion of genes for high intelligence. If they are below the average in capacity for intelligence, the proportion of genes for high intelligence will be reduced accordingly. Since good intelligence and socially valuable traits of character appear to be related, both traits would be affected. This is a simplification of a complicated genetic situation which need not be entered into detail here; the broad generalization made above is sufficiently correct for use in our attempt to forecast future trends in heredity.

The question we must consider is whether, in populations where the small family system is firmly established, there will be sufficient variations from the average to provide for the improvement of hereditary qualities from one generation to another. The answer will depend on the psychological attitudes of the people; these will be determined by a variety of pressures: cultural, economic, moral, religious, and their own self-interest. As there is no way of forecasting what these pressures will be a generation from now or beyond, it would be foolish to hazard a guess about the hereditary changes to be expected in the future. Recent trends in the United States appear favorable to genetic improvement, but they give no evidence of what would happen under changed conditions of society, which we may certainly expect in the near future.

While it is not at present possible to forecast what changes will take place in the frequency and distribution of the hereditary factors that make for high intelligence and character, it can be said with considerable certainty that great changes could take place, and that they could be of a sort to raise the whole level of human life.

Quite apart from the matter of the general level of intelligence and character, there are other aspects of genetic change on which there is a considerable base for speculation. Numerous studies have shown that under modern conditions of communication, transportation, education, and urban life there is an increase in assortative mating, that is, in the mating of like with like. People of similar tastes and interests meet and mingle far more easily today than in the past. To an increasing extent, marriages are based not on immediate proximity or even social class, but on community of interests, levels of education, levels of intelligence, or special abilities. Far more than in the past, musicians tend to marry musical acquaintances, athletes to marry athletes, physicists to marry physicists or their relatives. There is every reason to believe that this trend will continue. If it does, we may expect a continuing increase in the number of highly specialized people, and at a constantly higher level of competence in their particular specialty.

Recent experience indicates clearly that every race and every large population groupings includes a considerable proportion of people with highly specialized abilities. It is interesting to speculate about what will happen if assortative mating breaks national and racial boundaries. Already we have in the United States great numbers of able specialists driven by wars and dictatorships from Europe, and not an inconsiderable number from Asia. Not only are such changes of residence going on all over the world as one or another center attracts people of a particular type, but conventions and meetings of every sort—medicine, sports, every branch of science, arts and crafts, music—are no longer limited to participants from the country in which they are held, but draw on visitors from all over the world to discuss their specialty. It is quite possible, and even in the long run probable, that the kind of assortative mating of which we are speaking will spread beyond national boundaries to include all countries and peoples. If this happens, the future will find in one country or another groupings of family stocks specialized in some particular common ability, purebred for their specialty, but mongrels in the old sense of descent by race or national origin. Genes for particular types of ability would be concentrated in particular groups, but the aggregate frequency of such specialized genes would not change except insofar as one group or another had a higher or a lower rate of birth than the average of the population as a whole.

The assortative mating of people with specialized abilities does not imply that races and nations will mix into a single physical type. Assortative mating for physical characteristics such as color of skin, body build, and facial appearance will of course continue among the mass of the world's people. Some may hold that the increased movement of peoples will bring about a complete mixture of races. But such an expectation does not take into account the strongly documented evidence that, given the chance, like tends to marry like. There will of course be much intermarrying between different racial stocks, but it is quite possible that the future will see the mass of the world's people still grouped by race and proud of their race and culture. The racial mixtures of the past have generally been the results of war and of conquest, with many matings in which the woman had little choice. If the better world of the future is one of continued peace and equality, the voluntary system of mating and marriage may result in less race mixture and more selection within each race than past systems based on slavery or conquest. The superior races of the future will then be those who breed most from their own superior stocks and least from their poorest stocks.

The qualities of the men and women who will be carrying on man's destiny in the years ahead, their number and the proportions of each different kind, will be determined not by any process of "natural" selection, but by the voluntary decisions of individual men and women, each expressing his instinctive needs as modified by all the pressures and influences of his particular environment. The future of man is in his own hands. The possibilities are beyond the imagination of men today. If the hereditary factors underlying high intelligence and character were raised from the present average level to the level of, for instance, those 25% who are highest in such genetic qualities at the present time, problems of education and character building would take on an entirely new aspect. If, at the same time, a majority of this selected group were raised in homes equally above the average in the quality of care and example given the children, and were educated in schools appropriate to their above-average abilities, the quality of human life would everywhere be raised to an extraordinary degree.

Such a possibility is not difficult to envisage. It could be approximated in a very few generations if, in every walk of life, the couples who stand above their immediate neighbors in desirable qualities should bear an average of four children (not much above their present average of three) and the people who stand below the average in desirable qualities should bear an average of two (not much below their present average). Not all of the improvement would be genetic, since genetic factors are only part of what goes into making a superior man, and since children are only to a certain degree genetically similar to their parents. But on the whole superior children are raised in superior homes, whatever their economic or social level, and children tend to approximate the genetic as well as the cultural status of their parents. Nor would the change in each generation be as great as might be indicated by the superior couples having twice as many children as the couples below the average, for none of these groups are of "pure" stocks and their children would vary over a considerable range. But the change would take place far faster than any similar change effected by natural selection and would be reflected almost immediately and with cumulative results.

Will man in the near future maintain a social, economic, and psychological climate that could bring about such a result? He certainly has in his hands the power to do so. The cynic will deny such possibilities; but that would be to say that the long road man has traveled to reach his present state has come to an end in our generation. It seems more likely that we are only part way on our course, and that an open and hopeful road lies ahead.

References

Chapter 1

1 For material in the early part of this chapter, the author is in part indebted to the following articles which appeared in the *Scientific American*, September, 1960: Sherwood Washburn, "Tools and Human Evolution"; Marshall Sahlins, "The Origin of Society"; Charles F. Hockett, "The Origin of Speech"; William M. Howells, "The Distribution of Man"; and Robert J. Brachwood, "The Agricultural Revolution." He is also in part indebted to Henry F. Osborn, *Men of the Old Stone Age*, Charles Scribner & Sons, New York, 1914.

2 Sahlins, *op. cit.*

3 John B. Griffin, "Education and Size of Family in China," *Journals of Heredity*, vol. 17, no. 8, September, 1926, pp. 331–337.

4 J. Loessing Buck, *Land Utilization in China*, Council on Economic and Cultural Affairs, 1937. cf. Notestein and Chi-Ming Chiao, chap. XIII, p. 358.

5 Edward D. Driver, *Differential Fertility in Central-India*, Princeton University Press, Princeton, N.J., 1963.

6 John Cobb, Harry Raulet, and Paul Harper, "An IUD Field Trial in Lulliani, West Pakistan" Annual Meeting of APHA, October 21, 1965.

7 Harry Raulet, letter to Frederick Osborn, November 5, 1965.

Chapter 2

1 "President's News Conference," *New York Times*, December 3, 1959.

2 Based on data on average number of children ever born from the 1950 and 1960 Census. "Women by Number of Children Ever Born," 1950 Census, part 5, chap. C., "Fertility," and 1960 Census, Final Report, "Women by Number of Children Ever Born."

3 Part 2 of 1965 edition of *Health, Education, and Welfare Trends*, page 7: "State Data and State Ranking in H.E.W."

4 Ansley J. Coale, "Birth Rates, Death Rates, and Rates of Growth in Human Population" in Mindel C. Sheps and Jeanne Clare Ridley (ed.), *Public Health and Population Change*, University of Pittsburgh Press, Pittsburg, 1966, p. 245.

5 *Demographic Yearbook*, United Nations, 1965, Gross Reproduction Rates of Arab Countries.

6 Ronald Freedman, P. K. Whelpton, and Arthur A. Campbell, *Family Planning, Sterility and Population Growth*, McGraw-Hill, New York, 1959, p. 216.

7 *Ibid.,* p 32.

8 E. Lewis-Faning, "Report on an Enquiry into Family Limitation and Its Influence on Human Fertility during the Past

Fifty Years" Papers of the Royal Commission on Population, vol. 1, H.M. Stationery Office, London, 1949, p. 7.

9   Freedman, Whelpton, and Campbell, *op. cit.*, p. 65.

10 Frank Lorimer, Ellen Winston, and Louise Kiser, *Foundations of American Population Policy*, Harper Bros., New York, 1940, p. 16.

11 1950 and 1960 Census, *op. cit.*

12 Freedman, Whelpton, and Campbell, *op. cit.*, p. 120, table 4–12, and p. 121, table 4–13.

13 J. V. Higgins, Elizabeth Reed, and S. C. Reed in *Eugenics Quarterly*, vol. 9, no. 2, 1962, p. 89, table 7, and Carl Jay Bajema, "Estimation of the Direction and Intensity of Natural Selection in Relation to Human Intelligence," *Eugenics Quarterly*, vol. 10, no. 4, 1963, pp. 175–187.

14 Frederick Osborn, *Preface to Eugenics*, rev. ed., Harper & Bros., New York 1951, p. 175.

15 Higgins, Reed, and Reed, *op. cit.*

16 Bajema, *op. cit.*

17 1950 and 1960 Census, *op. cit.*

18 *Ibid.*

19 Ellsworth Huntington and Leon F. Whitney, *The Builders of America*, William Morrow & Co., New York, 1927.

20 Lewis M. Terman, and M. H. Oden, *Genetic Studies of Genius*, vol. V: *The Gifted Group at Middle Life*, Stanford University Press, Stanford, Calif., 1959, pp. 143–149.

Chapter 3

1 Lewis M. Terman and M. H. Oden, *Genetic Studies of Genius*, vol. V: *The Gifted Group at Middle Life*, Stanford University Press, Stanford, Calif., 1959, pp. 143–149.

2 cf. R. S. Woodward, "Heredity and Environment, A Critical Survey of Recently Published Material on Twins and Foster Children," Social Science Research Council, 1941, p. 23; R. M. C. Huntley, "Heritability and Intelligence," in *Genetics and Environmental Factors in Human Ability*, pp. 201–218, Oliver & Boyd, Edinburgh and London, 1966; Horatio H. Neuman, Frank N. Freeman, and Karl J. Holzinger, *Twins: A Study on Heredity and Environment*, University of Chicago Press, Chicago, 1937, pp. 73, 335, 344; and finally, James Shields, *Monozygotic Twins*, Oxford University Press, New York, 1962.

3 Anne Anastasi, *Differential Psychology*, 3rd ed., Macmillan, New York, 1965, p. 281.

4 Frederick Osborn, *Preface to Eugenics*, rev. ed., Harper & Bros., New York, 1951, p. 101.

5 N. D. M. Hirsch, "An Experimental Study of the East Kentucky Mountaineers," *Genetic Psychology Monograph*, 1928, pp. 183–244.

6 Osborn, *op. cit.* p. 116.

7 Frank Lorimer and Frederick Osborn, *Dynamics of Population*, Macmillan, New York, 1934, p. 140, based on data from Yerkes.

8   Terman, and Oden, *op. cit.*

9   Francis Galton, *Enquiries into Human Faculty*, Macmillan, London, 1883, p. 324.

10 Theodosius Dobzhansky, *Mankind Evolving*, Yale Univ. Press, 1962, p. 161. Table taken from Index of Opportunity of Selection by Crow and Spuhler, 1958–61. See also Dudley Kirk, "Demographic Factors Affecting the Opportunity for Natural Selection in the U.S.," *Eugenics Quarterly*, vol. 13, no. 3, September, 1966, pp. 271, 272.

11 Theodosius Dobzhansky, *Heredity and the Nature of Man*, Harcourt, Brace & World, New York, 1964.

Chapter 4

1   R. H. Post, "Population Differences in Red and Green Color Vision Deficiency: A Review, and a Query on Selection Relaxation," *Eugenics Quarterly*, vol. 9, no. 3, September, 1962, and Correction in vol. 12, no. 1, March 1965.

2   H. Kalmus, *Diagnosis and Genetics of Defective Colour Vision*, Pergamon Press, New York, 1965, p. 86.

3   R. H. Post, "Population Differences in Vision Acuity: A Review, with Speculative Notes on Selection Relaxation." vol. 9, no. 4, December, 1962.

4   R. H. Post, *Eugenics Quarterly*, "Deformed Nasal Septa and Relaxed Selection," *Eugenics Quarterly*, vol. 13, no. 2, June, 1966.

5 R. H. Post, "Breast Cancer, Lactation, and Genetics," *Eugenics Quarterly*, vol. 13, no. 1, March, 1966.

6 R. W. Miller, *Journal of Chronic Disease*, vol. 16, 1963, pp. 31–54.[6a] Arnold Sorsby, *Journal of Medical Genetics*, vol. 1, 1964, pp. 63–68.

7 *Human Genetics and Public Health*, World Health Organization Technical Report Series No. 282. Columbia University Press, New York, 1964, pp. 8–10.

8 Theodosius Dobzhansky, *Mankind Evolving*, Yale University Press, New Haven, Conn., 1962, p. 46.

9 Brace, C. C. and Montagu, M. F. Ashley, *Man's Evolution*, Macmillan, New York, 1965, p. 56.

10 James V. Neel, Margery W. Shaw, and William J. Schull, (ed.), *Genetics and the Epidemiology of Chronic Diseases*, U.S. Department of Health, Education, and Welfare, Public Health Service Publication No. 1163, February, 1965, p. 250.

11 Dobzhansky, *op. cit.*, p. 107.

12 *Ibid.*, p. 117.

13 *Human Genetics and Public Health*, *op. cit.*, p. 10.

14 Franz J. Kallmann, and D. Reisner, "Percentage Frequency of Tuberculosis in the Famiiles of 308 Tubercular Twins," *American Review of Tuberculosis*, vol. 47, 1943.

15 Curt Stern, *Principles of Human Genetics*, 2d ed., W. H. Freeman & Co., San Francisco, Calif., 1960, p. 562.

16 *Ibid.*, p. 670. Cf. also Dobzhansky, *op. cit.*, p. 28.

17 Franz J. Kallmann, *Heredity in Health and Mental Disorder,* W. W. Norton, New York, 1953

18 Irving I. Gottesman and James Shields, "Schizophrenia in Twins," *British Journal of Psychiatry,* vol. 112, no. 489, August, 1966.

19 *Human Genetics and Public Health, op. cit.,* p. 12.

20 *Ibid.*

21 *Ibid.*

22 *Ibid.*

23 *Ibid.*

24 Dobzhansky, *op. cit.,* p. 121.

25 *Ibid.,* p. 50.

26 Stern, *op. cit.,* p. 454.

27 *Ibid.,* p. 463.

28 *Ibid.,* p. 464.

29 Dobzhansky, *op. cit.,* p. 143.

30 *Ibid.,* p. 146.

31 *Ibid.,* p. 144.

32 Stern, *op. cit.,* p. 463.

33 Dobzhansky, *op. cit.,* p. 293.

34 C. P. Richter, "Rats, Man and the Welfare State," *American Psychology,* vol. 14, 1959, pp. 18–28.

35 H. J. Muller, "Our Load of Mutations," *American Journal of Human Genetics*, vol. 2, no. 111, p. 76.

36 Dobzhansky, *op. cit.*, p. 287.

Chapter 5

1 Francis Galton, *Enquiries into Human Faculty*, Macmillan, London, 1883, pp. 325–337.

2 R. L. Dugdale, *The Jukes*, G. P. Putnam's Sons, New York, 1877.

3 H. H. Goddard, *The Kallikak Family*, Macmillan, New York, 1912.

4 H. J. Muller, "Means and Aims in Human Genetic Improvement," *The Control of Human Heredity and Evolution*, T. M. Sonneborn, (ed.), MacMillan, New York, 1965.

5 Muller, H. J. "What Genetic Course Will Man Steer," Proceedings of the Third International Congress of Human Genetics, Chicago, September, 1966.

6 Curt Stern, *Principles of Human Genetics*, 2d ed. W. H. Freeman & Co., San Francisco, Calif., 1960, p. 294.

7 *Human Genetics and Public Health*, World Health Organization Technical Report Series No. 282, Columbia University Press, New York, 1964.

8 Helen G. Hammons, eds., 17 authors, *Heredity Counseling*, Paul B. Hoeber Inc., 1959, Harper and Row.

9 Holmes, Oliver Wendell, Buck vs. Bell, 274 U.S. 200–207 (1927).

10 J. E. Meade and A. S. Parkes, (eds.), *Biological Aspects of Social Problems*, Eugenics Society Symposia, vol. 1, 1964, Oliver & Boyd, London.

11 C. J. Witsop, Jr., C. J. MacLean, P. G. Schmidt, J. L. Henry, "Medical and Dental Findings in the Brandywine Isolate," *Alabama Journal of Medical Sciences*.

12 Frederick Osborn, "Excess and Unwanted Fertility," *Eugenics Quarterly*, vol. 10, no. 2, 1963, pp. 59–72.

13 Lee N. Robbins, *Deviant Children Grow Up*, Williams and Wilkins Co., Baltimore, 1966, p. 304.

14 Frederick Osborn, *Preface to Eugenics*, rev. ed., Harper & Bros. 1951, pp. 282–292, for a more extended discussion of this matter.

Index

Abnormalities, 63-82, 110-111; frequency of, 73-79

Abortions, 27

Adaptability, 11

Agricultural peoples, survival among since 8,000 BC, 13-18

Apes, 8

Asia, selection in, 14-17

Assortive mating, 114-115

Besant, 21

Birth, genetic change resulting from group differentials, 56-58; genetic significance of group and individual differentials, 41-62; group differentials in 24-32; individual differentials in 32-40

Birth control, 59-60, 92-94, 98-99, 108-109, 111; its effect on survival, 19-32; methods of, 22

Brain, development of, 10

Carrier, 95

China, selection in, 14-15

Chromosomes, 71-72; see also Genes

Colorblindness, as a case for relaxed selection, 66-67

Contraception, 59-60, 92-94, 98-99, 108-109, 111; its effect on survival, 19-32; types of, 22

Darwin, Charles, 1, 3, 83

Death rate, in United States, 19-20, 26; reduction of, 109-110

Defects, 63-82, 110-111; constitutional, 75-76; frequency of, 73-79; mental, 74-75; of diseases, 74; proposal for reduction of, 89-98

Demography, 4-5

Deuteranomoly, 66

Deuteranopia, 66

Dobzhansky, Theodosius, 73, 82; quoted, 61

Driver, Edward D., 15

Education, as a factor in heredity, 17, 51

Eisenhower, Dwight D., quoted, 21-22

Environment, among primitive hunters, 9; and heredity, 2, 42-44; and selection, 11-13; importance of, 11-12; improving, 102-106

Eugenics, defined, 1; history of proposals, 83-89; policies and proposals for, 83-106

Evolution, 1-4, 7

Family, size affecting genetic change in, 58-62; see also Birth control

Fertility differentials, among graduates of Harvard, Princeton, and Yale, 38-39

Galton, Francis, 84-85, 86; quoted, 52

Genes, 3-4, 42, 65, 70-72, 76-79, 90, 97, 112, 114; dominant, 71, 77, 78, 90, 97; recessive, 61, 71, 77

Genetic change, as a result of differentials in size of family between individuals, 58-62; resulting from group differentials in birth, 56-58

Genetic code, 3, 42, 44, 46

Genetic equilibrium, 79-82

Genetic load, 79-82

Heredity, and environment, 2; clinics, 91-92, 94; future of, 107-117; physical basis of, 70-72

Hirsch, N. D., 48

Holmes, Oliver Wendell, 92

Huntington, Ellsworth, 38

Immunity, 69-70

Intelligence, 11, 33-37, 39-40; environment and heredity and, 43; measuring heredity component, 41-53; proposal for raising level of, 98-106; tests, 44-45, 50-51; see also IQ

Income, as a factor in heredity, 17

India, selection in, 15-16

Industrialization, effects on birth, 24

Industrial Revolution, 18
Insemination, 86-89
IQ, 33-37, 39-40, 44-62 *passim*,
    98; *see also* Intelligence

Juke, 84, 85

Kallikak, 84, 85
Kallmann, Franz J., 74

Mankind Evolving, 73
Mendel, Gregor Johann, 3, 84
Mortality rate, in United States,
    19-20, 26; *see also* Death
    rate
Muller, H. J., 86-89; quoted, 82
Mutation, 4, 11, 61, 66, 71-72,
    76-79, 80, 89, 97; defined,
    71
Myopia, as a case for relaxed se-
    lection, 67-68

Nasal septa, as a case for relaxed
    selection, 68

Origin of Species, The, 1
Osborn, J. J., 38

Pakistan, selection in, 15-16
Personality, measuring heredity
    components of, 41-53
Phillips, John C., 38
Planned Parenthood Federation,
    22
Population, of Homo sapiens dur-
    ing stone age, 11

Protanomaly, 66
Protanopia, 66
Psychology, 4-5, 25, 42, 58; tests,
    44-45

Race, 50-51, 115; origin of, 11
Richter, C. P., 82

Sahlins, Marshall, quoted, 9
Sanger, Margaret, 21
Selection, 6-18; and birth control,
    19-32; education and in-
    come as a factor in, 17;
    evidence for relaxed, 64-
    70; explanation of, 12-13;
    in Asia, 14-17; index of
    opportunity for, 53-56; re-
    laxed, 81, 111
Sex, 9; repression of, 9
Sterilization, 92, 95
Survival, 6-18

Terman, Lewis M., 39
Truman, Harry S., 22

United States, death rate in, 19-
    20, 26; survival of family
    lines in, 19-40
Urbanization, effects on birth, 24

Wallace, Bruce, 82
Welfare state, effect on birth, 22;
    survival in, 26
Welpton, Pascal K., 29
Whitney, Leon, 38